To the Philippines
with Love

To the Philippines with Love

by Lorraine Carr

with a special introduction

by General Carlos P. Romulo

Sherbourne Press, Inc.
Los Angeles, California

In memory of
RAMÓN MAGSAYSAY
Leader of the Philippines

Acknowledgments

DESCRIPTION OF COCKFIGHTS:
Noli me Tangere, by Jose Rizal

HISTORY OF CORREGIDOR:
Combat History Division,
United States Army Forces
Western Pacific—AFWESPAC

OFFICIAL DATES ON PHILIPPINE HISTORY:
Forbes history of the Philippine Islands
The Philippine Islands

THE RAMON MAGSAYSAY SPEECH:
The Magsaysay Story, by Carlos P. Romulo
and Marvin M. Gray

Introduction

ᴏᴮᴇᴏ THE EFFORT OF understanding another country is a difficult one. Such attempts rarely succeed as fiction and, in the body of literature in the world with an international theme, few works have succeeded in truly depicting the actuality and ambiguity of a culture different from that of the writer's.

Of the books on Asia, in fiction form, there are still fewer examples of satisfactory achievements. One thinks of the now classic *Passage to India* by E. M. Forster and the books on China by Pearl Buck. In the case of these two authors, the success seems to derive from what Keats would call *negative capability*—the capacity of these writers to assimilate the ambiguous suggestions of the realities in the countries they wrote about without trying to subsume details under specific and formulated categories. In short, they were able to create the Oriental reality in terms of its human fact, avoiding the easy surrender to types in the delineation of character and the pat formulation of simplistic political conclusions.

To the Philippines with Love by Lorraine Carr is one of the rare books, in fiction form, on the Philippine reality. Its style is highly evocative and it depicts, with both irony and a tenderness that could come only with intimacy of her subject, the paradoxes and myths and class superstitions of the human condition in the country.

Philippine society presents a lot of difficulty to the understand-

9

ing of a consciousness which has been conditioned by egalitarian principles. Here the aspirations of people are all democratic, but they instinctively relate themselves to each other in terms of the notion of class. Christianity, or more particularly, Hispanic Catholicism, has reinforced the Oriental fatalism of our peasantry into making them passively accept the hierarchy of classes in society. They take the difference of their lot as a condition, and the Filipino boy from a peasant family, like Niño in Lorraine Carr's book, tends to his situation in life with the joy and innocent pleasure of one who knew, secretly, how the lilies were clothed. The author catches this accurately in her depiction of the boy:

> "Despite hardships, Niño had a happy disposition. He sat under the big mango tree and shined shoes for the family, and sang as he worked. At night, when the chores were done, he would stand under the stars and sing. I used to watch him from my bedroom window. He stood erect with his chest out, living the song he sang, using gestures as if he were a star on a stage. Suddenly the concert ended, for the landlady would scream at him to stop the noise and get to bed. He would walk slowly toward the garage, still humming softly as if he must finish the song he had started."

This is an insight comparable to Mark Twain's experience with the Negro boy in his autobiography which became the basis for his famous character in *Huckleberry Finn*, Jim. Lorraine Carr does not flinch from the truth of the reality she writes about. She integrates into her sense of milieu the harsh and the simple human fact, faithfully recording the contrast and conflict of innocence and brutal calculation in the way Filipinos relate themselves to each other.

Other books by foreigners about the Philippines fail as literature because their writers react to Filipino life with definite and sometimes ready prejudices and sympathies. They are either shocked by our color and size, or they become sentimental over our history and the present terms of our life. In either case, truth is falsified and fiction becomes an unwholesome vehicle of prejudice or faked emotions.

To the Philippines with Love is a book of art and high intelligence. Its autobiographical aspect does not disqualify it as pure literature, and the ordering that Miss Carr has made of her experience in the country does not diminish its authenticity as a faithful document, seen through the vision of a foreigner, of Philippine society in the years immediately after the Second World War.

This, I believe, is the highest merit of Lorraine Carr's book: writing about a country not her own, living with people totally different from her, she is nevertheless equal to the moral challenge of her task, which is to present Filipinos not as exotic farmers, genteel middleclasses, or arrogant aristocrats or even as a different race, but as human beings. Society, the Western traveler must perhaps be continually told—any society—is not a display window for his horrified or lachrymose inspection but is a unit of the whole human community. Lorraine Carr's triumph in this book is of the highest moral and social journalism.

Carlos P. Romulo

Carlos P. Romulo has completed almost a quarter of a century of service to his country as a soldier and as a statesman. Prior to World War II, he had been one of the leading newspaper publishers in Manila. He is widely known to Americans as a lecturer and author. He won the Pulitzer Prize for distinguished correspondence in 1941. He is the author of seven books.

Born in Manila in 1901, he was graduated from the University of the Philippines in 1918 and three years later received his master's degree from Columbia University. He now holds honorary degrees from twenty-seven other institutions.

His career of government service, at home and abroad, reached a first climax when he was elected president of the Fourth General Assembly of the United Nations. He has served as Philippine Ambassador to the United States. He is currently serving as president of the University of the Philippines and also serves as Minister of Education on President Ferdinand Marcos' staff of Cabinet ministers. General Carlos P. Romulo is recognized in the Far East, in the United States, and throughout the world as one of the most influential leaders in the Philippines today.

Lorraine Carr

To the Philippines
with Love

Chapter One

THE DAY MY HUSBAND, Doctor William E. ("Huddy") Huddleston, came home, shortly after the peace with Japan was signed aboard the battleship *Missouri* on September 2, 1945, with travel orders to Manila, Philippines, I was out in my garden tending my rose bushes, hoping they might bloom before we moved to a new station. It was not to be. You do not argue with Uncle Sam about a rose bush when things need to be done in the Philippines many thousand miles away.

I surrendered the rose bushes to the bugs and walked arm in arm with him inside our apartment. Move again? My heart sank at the very thought of it. We had moved so many times during the war—seven moves in one year—and had lived in everything from a pup tent to our present apartment in San Antonio, Texas! I glanced about the lovely room in which we had been settled exactly six weeks. His eyes, too, swept the luxury of the room. Then, as if to apologize, he said: "They need me in Manila."

He had asked for this foreign assignment unbeknownst to me, yet I had known all during the dark days of the war, his heart was in the Philippines. He had been medical director of the "Fighting 200th" Division of Coast Artillery in Taos, New Mexico. He had been unable to follow the boys, to take his stand with them in the last dark days on Corregidor, or perhaps trudge along with them in the Bataan Death March. Yes, I knew he had to go. I closed my eyes and recalled recent pictures I had seen of Manila: the most devastated city in the world, except Warsaw. I could see the gaunt, ghost-like buildings with blackened pieces of iron sticking out like the charred entrails of a chicken; I could see pot-bellied children and hear their cries of hunger; women in tattered garments scraping the earth for a cupful of dirty rice; families living in squalor under pieces of tin for a roof; looting, killing. I seemed to hear the rat-tat-tat of a machine-gun over the roof tops in the areas where the Japs were still cornered.

Once more I surveyed my lovely apartment, then before my eyes rose the vision of a bleak little quonset hut beside Manila Bay, a little quonset that would be rocked by earthquakes and lashed by typhoons. I could see a battle-weary army jeep jumping over shell holes in the streets of Manila and chugging along in mud hub-deep. I glanced at him sitting by the window in the comfortable blue-upholstered chair. He was very quiet, just waiting for me to speak.

He was a graduate of the Army Medical School, Washington, D.C.—the West Point in medicine. The graduates of this great old school were scattered to the four corners of the earth serving their flag. Soldiers without guns.

I knew in my heart that he had to go to the Philippines; he had to stalk the bleak shores of Corregidor; walk through Big Malinta Tunnel and strain his ears to hear a familiar cry—a cry for help; he must see Bataan, Ft. Santiago and the grim prison walls of Cabanatuan; he must tiptoe ever so quietly among the white crosses at Military Cemetery No. 2, the famous Balintawak, for here many of his boys lay sleeping. These boys he could not help, but their comrades, the Filipinos, who had fought so heroically by their side, needed him. Yes, he must go. To him it was a job unfinished.

An hour ago I would have said that nothing on earth could separate me from this comfortable apartment. Now, I must make it easier for him. Gently I placed my hand on his shoulder. "Huddy? When do we leave?"

"I go tomorrow," he said. "You'll come later; no dependents can go at this time."

He was off to Manila. His plane lifted and soared high in the air. I watched it until it was but a tiny speck, then it passed out of sight. Had he done the right thing? My heart asked over and over. He had just gained the assignment he had wanted in this San Antonio station, and it was a comparatively easy one. Now, he was going forth to assume a big job and to work under conditions that were seemingly impossible. How would he fare?

Luckily we could not foresee the strain Huddy was to endure in the next five years in the post-war Philippines, else we might have taken second thought. We might have remained in old San Antonio sitting comfortably in the big blue chairs. I recall he drank a glass of milk at the airport as we were waiting for the plane. "I love milk," he said, and ordered a second glass. How were we to know that he would not see a glass of fresh milk for another five years? Nor did he know, as he emerged from a warm tub bath an hour before coming out to the airport, that he would not have another warm bath for that many years. These things we did not know. And it was for the best.

I was sad when I returned to the apartment. Already I felt the many miles, the many months that were to come between the meeting of my husband and myself again. I busied myself and cried a little as I watered the rose bushes and slapped at the bugs. It would have been comforting for me to know, at that moment, that very soon I would be in the land of orchids—in the far-away Philippines—that I would wear orchids in my hair from dawn till dark, having a fresh one every hour, if I chose. That I would trim a Christmas tree with orchids; that the tall cool drinks served before dinner would have tiny butterfly orchids floating on top instead of mint; that a platter of rice would be garnished, not with ordinary parsley, heavens no! but with little purple orchids.

I knew the wait would be long, for no dependents could sail for the Orient until quarters were available. And since first things come first, the building of quarters for dependents was not considered urgent. Besides, there was a backlog of 8,000 wives and children to follow their men to Japan, China, and the Philippines.

July in San Antonio is an unbearably hot month, so I gave up the luxurious apartment and moved back to Taos, New Mexico, my former home, and took a studio at the Harwood Foundation. I was joined by my seventeen-year-old stepdaughter, Harvel. We settled down for months of waiting. And in this interim we read every book we could find on the Philippines to acquaint ourselves with the climate so we would know how to make up a wardrobe. Each author who had lived in the islands had a different story. One said it was stifling hot twelve months out of the year; another said the coldest he had ever been in his life was in Manila one January night.

Even before I left San Antonio I had conferred with army wives who had lived in Manila before the war. The wives were about as contradictory as the authors. One said, "Take nothing but cotton clothes. And you always wear a long dress after six o'clock." I was told not to take leather shoes, for during the rainy season a six-inch beard will grow over night on the toe of a leather shoe. Gold slippers? Heavens no! They'd tarnish. So it sort of simmered down that a pair of tennis shoes would be the kind likely to hold up in the islands. But they would look sadly out of place with the long skirt after six o'clock. Another wife said to be sure and take along a coat, for you'd shiver many a night. Sure, said she, take silk dresses, leather shoes, gold slippers, and a raincoat. One army wife had hated the Philippines and the Filipinos; another had dearly loved the islands and its people and had cried her eyes out when she had had to leave.

After Huddy had been in Manila a few weeks, I dispatched a letter which instructed him to keep his eyes open around the

Army and Navy Club and let me know just what the women were wearing. I didn't expect much information from him, for I could wear a new dress each day and likely he would never notice it until the bills arrived. Then he might ask, "Oh, did you buy a new dress? Where is it?"

But in due time his answer to my letter arrived. Yes, he had been at the Army and Navy Club on Saturday night and he had noticed that all the women wore dresses. What a great help! I had assumed they did; however, in one of the books on the Philippines I had seen a picture of a barefoot Igorot woman wearing only a skirt wrapped sarong-like with absolutely no covering above the waist.

He continued by saying that I had evidently misunderstood the army wife about shoes. The women wear shoes; he knew because he had danced with Lou Kramer and he was certain she had on shoes for he had stepped on her toes a dozen times and she gave him "Old Ned" for skinning her toes. Now about stockings, no one wore them. The women sat around the Club with bottles of repellant they applied to their legs at intervals to keep off mosquitos. He ended by saying he hoped this was all the information we needed concerning our clothes. And would we please, please, hurry? He was very lonely for us.

Harvel and I pieced together all the information we had gathered and assembled a wardrobe of sorts, for we had a tentative sailing date. We packed our trunks, taking along a few precious books, the silverware, linens, and clothes. The trunks were locked, just waiting to be off to San Francisco. Then came the strike on the West Coast which tied up all commercial ships. It lasted for weeks.

In the meantime Huddy was dickering with Washington to fly us over. Never! Dependents did not fly; it was too expensive. So we must wait until we could get a ship, even a slow cattle boat, anything. Huddy got on his high horse. Medical officers were scarce, and if they wanted him to remain in the Philippines they would have to fly his family over. So they agreed to fly us if he would pay the difference between ship and plane. Never! He stood his ground. And he won. Here came orders to fly but we could take only fifty-five pounds of luggage.

We unlocked our trunks and packed our suitcases with the direst necessities. Naturally, Harvel had to take evening gowns and slippers, and since I expected to be doing newspaper work in Manila, I had to take along a portable typewriter (I was going to continue my writing, which I did under my single name, Lorraine Carr). The suitcases were packed and weighed. We waited. Then came another telegram saying that we were to go by ship. Again we hauled out the trunks and repacked them. We waited and waited. Five times we packed and unpacked from trunk to suitcase and the other way around.

Each day we hurried to the village post office hoping to find travel orders; none came. We haunted the Western Union office hoping for news that we might fly; none came. We gave up and settled down to spend the winter in Taos. When we passed by the Western Union office, we refused to even glance inside. I wonder why we thought such an attitude might hurry things up. One day, as we were passing, we were attracted by the young girl tapping on the window. She was flapping her arms like a sea gull. "We are flying," said Harvel, and rushed inside to get the message.

We had only twenty-four hours to get to San Francisco, and, at this point the trunks were packed to go by ship. We ran to the studio and dumped everything in the middle of the floor and packed our suitcases. We had many friends in Taos who dropped in to see us off. Some were irritated that dependents should go gallivanting around the world to join their men. While we basked in luxury in the Orient, they had to pay taxes to support the government. Such remarks raised my dander. Someone in these United States must give up the comforts of home to guard these far-away frontiers. Didn't they understand?

In my pocket was a letter from Huddy. He informed us the going in Manila was tough; we must not expect even the barest of necessities, for living in this war-torn area was a challenge, a matter of survival. He was billeted at the Avenue Hotel on Rizal Avenue, now taken over by the Army. Once it had been a swanky hostelry; now it was bullet-ridden. There were big holes in the walls and at night the rats crawled in and slept on his cot and nibbled on his toes. He had only one bed sheet and he had to sleep on an army blanket, hot as it was, while the house boy washed the sheet. There were no elevators; he had to climb eight flights of stairs three times a day, for the dining room was on the eighth floor. It was no life of luxury to which we were going. He had secured quarters, so the letter said, and judging from the description it was little more than a piece of rusty tin leaned up against a bombed-out wall. He told us to leave behind the brand new Mercury for only an army jeep could negotiate the streets of Manila which were filled with great shell holes. We were to bring no electrical appliances, not even an iron, for the current in Manila would not accommodate stateside electrical gadgets, except with step-down transformers and these were not to be had.

He apologized for even wanting us to join him in this war-torn country, the likes of which no human being could visualize. It was the toughest station to which he had ever been assigned.

I knew by the tone of his letter that other officers had been talking to him. Some of these men would not ask their wives to share these hardships. Did he feel ashamed that he had asked us to come? He had seemed so eager for us to share the experiences of the Orient with him. There were many wives who refused to go to Manila. They had good reasons, so they thought: comfortable homes in the old U.S.A., good schools and bridge clubs they could not leave. And they made dire predictions: I might get leprosy, and all the flesh would slip from my bones; I might be beheaded by a "Juramentado," a Moro gone amuck; and did

I know about the pythons in the islands? In the early days in
the Philippines if a soldier went AWOL, the authorities made a
search, and when they came upon a pair of shoes and helmet,
they wrote their report: "Soldier swallowed by a python!" Yes,
I was certain the husbands of these wives had been talking to
my husband. I read again: "Manila is beset with hardships and
dangers. I won't ask you to come. I'll try to get along without
you."

I rushed down to the Western Union office and sent the following cable: "Whither thou goest, I will go. Thy station shall
be my station. Thy jeep shall be my jeep."

It was November, 1946, when we arrived in San Francisco.
We went immediately to the transportation office to pick up
travel orders and to inquire as to the reliability of the Trans-
Ocean Lines on which we were booked for travel. I had never
heard of it. The clerk informed me he was very sure it was a safe
line since no crash had been reported.

Dressed in our best tweed suits with corsages of pink camellias,
we arrived at the airport across Bay Bridge to take passage for
Manila. About thirty people were on hand to make this flight,
and ten of this number were women. I was very much surprised
to find some of the women dressed in slacks, some in army
fatigue suits, and a couple in very plain seersucker suits. I kept
looking at their travel ensembles, and they were looking at mine.
No doubt they thought I was overdressed. And I was, I was
soon to learn.

I shall never forget my first glimpse of the old plane on which
we were to fly this vast expanse of the Pacific. It resembled a
great, droopy grasshopper, squatted on its rear, too disabled even
to flick a wing. "Will it fly?" I asked a man who was also eyeing
the old craft. "They don't know yet," was all he said.

By this time I was terrified at the thought of boarding this
discarded army number; and I was downright angry. After all,
dependents were entitled to first class passage. I immediately

telephoned the transportation office and took them to task for booking us on this old crate. "What do you think we are, Kamikazes?"

Very curtly a voice answered. "It is catch as catch can with everything on strike. Just be thankful you don't have passage on the back of a sea gull!" and bang went the receiver. I calmed down. The office had done the best it could and I must remember that transportation to the Orient was at a premium. So I decided that Harvel and I would take our chances with the others. We stepped in line to be weighed. And we were in for a surprise! When the office had wired us for our weight, like vain women, we had stepped on the scales stripped. Now we wore heavy coats, carried hand-bags that bulged with cosmetics, and toted along cameras and typewriters.

The old plane could not be overloaded. No one was allowed an extra pound. Those in charge of the flight went about frisking everyone to see that extra cameras were not concealed under the folds of a coat. I had made allowance for my typewriter, but I had intended to carry a bulky book manuscript in my arms; it was taken from me. A kind man on his way to Shanghai offered to carry the parcel for me, since he did not have his full allowance of fifty-five pounds.

Harvel and I were busy dumping jars of cold cream and twenty bars of soap in the middle of the floor. Mr. Peralta of the Philippines, who was a passenger en route home after a refresher course in law at Harvard, offered to take our cosmetics on his weight allowance. We must take the soap, he told us, for soap was a dollar a bar in Manila, if you could find it at all.

So we were off to Manila. We boarded the old plane with about as much enthusiasm as Jonah entered the belly of the whale. It was an old bucket-seated plane, peppered with bullet holes. As I sat down on the pieces of laced rope that made the seats, the tough fiber of the hemp probed right through the skirt of my good Davidow suit. By the time I had reached my destination, would there be a seat in my skirt?

Suddenly I went sentimental. I seemed to see young American boys—frightened boys—strapping themselves in the bucket seats opposite me, taking off for battle zones. The bullet holes were proof that more than once the old crate had flown over enemy territory, and no doubt had come in for many a landing with red lights blinking. At least we were not taking off to encounter enemy fire. We were on a luxury trip, or so our tax-paying friends had told us.

I felt ashamed that I had complained because we were not to fly on a plush job. I glanced at my pink camellias; I knew I could not wear them. I unpinned the corsage and tried to cover it with my purse. Harvel, looking at the bullet holes, removed her corsage too. We glanced at each other but did not speak. Later, when the plane had gained enough altitude to permit us to unfasten our safety belts, we slipped to the rest room and stuffed the pink camellias in an urp cup.

We were scarcely thirty minutes in the air, when the "Sacred Carabao," as we had christened the old plane, was in trouble. A dead engine. The pilot turned around and headed back to San Francisco. As soon as we landed, a crew of mechanics with tools in their hands came running toward the plane as if they had anticipated this trouble. They got on with the patching job. We waited all through the night and the next day before the old plane could get off the ground.

At seven in the evening we took off. The engines appeared to be on good behavior so on we winged to Honolulu.

The purser brought out air mats and spread them in the passage of the plane, and exhausted from our long wait, we bedded down like cattle. By this time I was ready to trade my good tweed suit for a pair of army fatigues and mentally I complimented the women on the way they were dressed for this flight. I slept next to a man who snored all night, and Harvel was crowded against the door by a big, fat woman who held a baby in her arms. Even though the door was wired together, I worried for fear it might fall off and we would lose them in mid-ocean.

At break of dawn I was aroused by the sputtering of one engine; it was belching fire. I was relieved to see Diamond Head looming up and felt sure the pilot could bring the plane down in Honolulu so the men could patch it up again. And he did. Once more a crew of mechanics took over. Eight hours later we were on our way.

We made it to Johnston Island, that tiny little speck of land that is scarcely big enough to house a crew of mechanics. We stopped only to refuel. The landing strip is so short, when the nose of the "Sacred Carabao" was lifted the hind wheels were dragging in the water. It was a tricky bit of maneuvering; I was so impressed I sent a note up to the pilot and congratulated him on his skill.

By the time we reached Kwajalein I had acquired a sort of pioneer spirit, such as my grandmother had when she traveled by covered wagon down the Old Santa Fé Trail. Grandmother, I'm told, had laughed at hardships, such as wild Indians who flourished tomahawks, blinding blizzards, and starvation. Once when the wagon wheel fell to staves, she calmly pitched camp under a pine tree until grandfather could fell a tree and hew out a new wheel. But to be an atomic-age pioneer meant battling typhoons, man-eating sharks, and what on earth did one do if the old plane fell to staves? Even grandmother's hair would have stood on end at the thought of pitching camp atop a white-capped wave in mid-Pacific, until a new plane could be built.

It had been five days since we left San Francisco. When we arrived at Guam, we voted the "Sacred Carabao" a most accommodating plane. It had limped over the vast stretches of the Pacific and broken down regularly on the islands. But at Guam all was going well. Even the mechanics looked disappointed as they stuffed their pliers back into hip pockets.

We had breakfast in Guam, and about an hour's delay. Harvel and I spent the time refreshing ourselves. We had a spit bath using a cake of soap I had smuggled in my purse. We changed into lighter clothes for it was very warm in Guam, and our woolen suits were uncomfortable. I dressed in a lovely brown linen suit with a small matching hat, very Vogue-ish-looking; Harvel wore an attractive ensemble of black linen. We had bought our clothes in San Francisco and wanted to look attractive when we arrived in Manila, for the doctor was very proud of "his girls."

We were boarding the plane for Manila and would arrive at three in the afternoon. Someone cheerfully called out: "Manila or bust!" I was standing right under the gasoline tank in line to board the plane. I too, took up the cry. "Manila or bust!" Then splash! Splash! A dozen rivets, or so it seemed to me, popped out of the gas tank and I was drenched with gasoline. The old plane was once again handed over to the mechanics to be patched up. They had their doubts but taxied the plane away to get on with the job.

I was consigned to an Army nurse to be scrubbed from head to foot. My baggage was rolled away with the plane and the brown linen suit was rinsed out and hung up to dry. The nurse dressed me in a fatigue suit, one of those green mottled numbers camouflaged to resemble a tree or a tiger creeping through the jungle. Never mind. I could change my clothes when the "Sacred Carabao" was rolled back.

During this interlude the Army gave us luxurious jeep trips along the beautiful shore line of Guam where the water looks like blue, blue ink. We stopped at a little store, way out on the far side of the island, and I spied a large can of Schilling black pepper for twenty-five cents. I reached for the can, for we had done without pure black pepper for many months in the States. Harvel stayed my hand. Why clutter up my purse or overload the plane when the Army Commissary had plenty of black pepper? Reluctantly I replaced the can. A week later in Manila I paid one peso for one tablespoon of pepper that was mixed with sand.

At Guam we had time to get acquainted with Mr. Peralta who had been kind enough to carry our cosmetics in his luggage. He was a lawyer and the father of two daughters who were to enroll in the University of the Philippines. Harvel would also enroll there the next week. He wanted his daughters to get acquainted with an American girl. We exchanged addresses so we might get in touch with each other at a later date.

A few minutes later, an American man, who was returning to the islands to re-enter a business, called me aside. He had overheard my conversation with Mr. Peralta. He took it upon himself to brief me about my conduct during my stay in the Philippines. I should not, under any circumstances, let my stepdaughter associate with these girls. To do so would be to lose face. The Americans had always kept the Filipinos in their place. These standards, he said, were set by the dignified American Embassy.

His advice didn't sit well with me. I glanced at our lawyer friend who had so willingly assisted us with our overweight parcels. He was well-dressed, dignified, and educated. He was kind and helpful. No matter, said the American man, if a Filipino were a lawyer, a doctor from Yale, or the President of the Philippines, an American did not associate with him. I took him to task, "The Philippines were given their independence on July 4th, 1946. They are a free people the same as France, England, or America. Is your way of thinking democratic? Shall we keep the Filipinos on bended knees?" His answer was the same. "You are an American. Don't lose face." I stood tall and looked him straight in the eye. "I *shall* lose face, for I shall be a rebel." I turned and walked over to Mr. Peralta who was conversing with Harvel.

He smiled at me, then walked over to a trailing vine of

flowering cadeña de amor and gathered a few of the pink blossoms. He brought them to Harvel and twined them in her hair which was done in a braid on top of her head. "You are so beautiful and these beautiful flowers want to adorn your hair." It was such a gracious gesture. He ignored the remarks of the "Ugly American" which, no doubt, he had overheard. Rather he let the beauty of the flowers speak for him.

Orders were called at six o'clock in the evening to board the plane. We were scheduled to arrive at Manila at three in the morning, "God willing," said the pilot. By this time most of the passengers were apprehensive. I could hear: "We'll never make it." "We should have waited until daylight for it would be much easier to get into a rubber boat." The American, who had crabbed all the way, said: "I have a hunch we'll be down in one hour and my hunches are always right." This man had been a nuisance all the way; any one of us might have been tempted to pitch him overboard.

I kept my eye on a life belt just over my head and again and again in my mind reviewed the instructions of how to get into it. I saw others cautiously reading the page; all were tense. However, I was so weary after five days of limping from San Francisco, that I finally dozed off to sleep. Hours later I was aware that Harvel was shaking me vigorously. "Wake up! This is the end!" I grabbed for my life belt and was struggling to get into it. Then I heard a terrific, crashing sound. I prayed that death would come quickly for all of us.

It *was* the end. We had landed on a metal landing strip at the International Airport in Manila. So had ended our luxurious plane trip across the Pacific. Forgetting my tiger suit, I rushed into Huddy's arms. He was so overjoyed to see us he failed to notice my traveling ensemble until moments later. "Darling, have you no clothes?" When we explained our harrowing experiences aboard the "Sacred Carabao," he realized he was lucky to have us by his side.

Mr. Peralta came forward to return the cosmetics he had brought over for us. While he and Huddy were exchanging greetings, the American sidled up to me again to get in one last word. "Remember my advice." I simply glowered at him, but Harvel was not so kind. She didn't reply to his remark, merely stuck out her tongue at him.

After we had passed customs, Mr. Peralta instructed his driver to carry our baggage out to our car. Car? It was the most dilapidated old jeep ever to creep back from a battle zone. "How do you like my Rolls Royce?" asked Huddy. Harvel and I loved it and right away christened the old jeep "Adam." After the driver had loaded us in, Mr. Peralta waved good-bye, and we headed for Manila. I knew I would lose face in the Philippines, that is, by the standards of that American. I was going forth in this new land to give the best of my mind and spirit to my new neighbors. In return I was quite sure my neighbors, the Filipinos, would have much to offer me.

Chapter Two

❦ IT WAS THREE O'CLOCK in the morning when we arrived at our quarters in the Pasay district. Huddy knocked at the door and called to the landlady, Mrs. Respicio, who had waited up so she could lift the heavy iron bar which barricaded the front door. Every door in Manila was kept barricaded day and night. No one dared lift a bar until it was known who was knocking. For a thief needed only get a foot in a crack of the door; sometimes he even stole the door.

I shall never forget how pretty Mrs. Respicio looked in her rose-colored terno, the national costume. The floor-length skirt was made of sheer embroidered pina cloth; the fitted blouse had sleeves made of a stiff material that billowed out like butterfly wings. She wore an embroidered panatela over the blouse—this is a large collar that stands high at the neck and tucks in at the waist. There is a certain knack to the adjusting of a panatela, very much like the draping of a sari. Mrs. Respicio's dark hair was caught in a very large bun at the nape of her neck. She was beautiful and poised. She was a teacher in the public schools of Manila.

Huddy had secured this apartment through an ad he had inserted in the Manila *Times,* which she had answered. He went to look at the apartment, and rented it, but she refused to take any money in advance. She trusted him, even though she had never seen him before. She wanted to be kind. Her family had suffered so much during the war. With her three children she had slipped from barrio to barrio seeking food and shelter. During this time, her husband was in prison, and she had no way of knowing if he were alive or dead.

There were many little appointments in her home that spoke of gracious living in other days . . . beautiful mahogany floors, stairway and bathrooms made of Spanish tile. The Japs had moved into this home during The Occupation, and when the Americans had retaken the city, the little men of the Rising Sun had carted the lovely furniture and the books from the library to the outside and had burned them. They had removed most of the plumbing, even to the kitchen sink, and had taken the toilet seats. It was in this stripped-down manner that we set up housekeeping in Manila.

We were tired after our long plane flight so we went to our upstairs quarters. Huddy had secured army hospital beds on the usual memorandum sheet, and over these tall-legged beds were mosquito tents, the first I had ever seen. We put Harvel to bed and tucked the mosquito tent around her, then Huddy sprayed the rooms with a big DDT gun. I can assure you my husband would never take a prize for Interior Decorating, but you should have seen the king-sized bed he set up in our bedroom. Two tall army beds side by side, and he had fastened two mosquito tents together with nails to cover them. Bless him. The bed was very hard. No matter. We were together again.

Huddy arose early to go to the office. He would have breakfast at the Army and Navy Club, and I would sleep until noon.

All was quiet. Suddenly I felt a cold, clammy-like object crawling up my leg. Heavens! Was it a python? I let out a blood-curdling scream and lunged right through the mosquito tent. I had aroused the entire household, and the landlady was at our door immediately, no doubt expecting to find me on the floor with a bolo knife plunged through my innards.

My bed fellow proved to be a little gecko, a wee lizard that was nudging my leg rather kittenish-like—a very good sign, said Mrs. Respicio, for this little lizard was bidding me welcome to the islands. I didn't tell her so, but I would have preferred a brass band to do the honors. The Filipinos have great respect for the little geckos; every home has many of them, just as American homes have cats. These little salamanders have suction pads on the bottom of their feet that enable them to crawl over the ceiling. They eat gnats, flies, and mosquitos. Some of them are very tiny, like the one-gecko-welcoming committee in my bed; others are six inches long. All are harmless.

I learned to live with them; you must if you live in the Philippines. Most any night I'd find one at the head of my bed blinking his little pink eyes at me. I'd stick out my tongue and make a face; he'd blink the faster. Often in the mornings I'd find one of the wee ones in my shoe. Rather than having to face the geckos at each break of day, I took to going barefoot. If I went to my dressing table, a gecko might be napping on my powder puff; if I started to put sugar in my coffee, one might be in the sugar bowl. I was never brave enough to contain myself when I encountered one. Once I was walking down the Escolta and reached for a handkerchief in the pocket of my raincoat, and brought forth a gecko. I let out a scream that brought two policemen to my side. They relieved me of the tiny lizard, and one of them put the little fellow in the pocket of his shirt and buttoned down the flap. He would take it home to his wife; she just loved geckos.

I awoke early, my second morning in the Philippines, for strange sounds had wafted through my window. I heard the whack of the paddle as the lavandera washed and spanked the bed sheets to a snowy whiteness; the creaking wheels of a caratella as the people drove to market—all unfamiliar sounds at that moment, but later I would learn to listen for them and know it was the beginning of a new day in this fascinating land.

Then I heard a shrill voice, "Poot. Poot. Poot." I ran to the window to look out. Below stood a Filipino lad dressed in khaki shorts, just plain old G.I. underwear, and nothing more. Did the poor fellow forget to put on his pants? Then, down the street came a group of men dressed in the same manner. Surely all of them couldn't be so absent-minded. Over his shoulder the vendor carried a bamboo pole about four feet long, and, dangling at each end was a bamboo basket filled with tiny parcels wrapped in banana leaves. These packages held sweet rice cakes. The Filipinos breakfast on them as they walk down the street, or as they ride a bus to work. Soon a crowd had gathered under my window to bargain with the "puto" vendor. There were men in underwear, men in white starched suits, women in native dresses, and naked children—all of them buying puto.

Down the street came a very thin old woman with a large bamboo tray filled with beans, tomatoes, cucumbers, and onions balanced on her head. She called out "gulay, gulay" (vegetables) and a few women gathered to make their daily purchases from this market stall atop her head. Her companion's head tray was filled with squawking chickens with tied feet. The women looked gaunt and hungry, and their thin hands resembled the claws of birds.

The street drama passed on. I looked down on the banana trees loaded with fruit, then to the tall papaya tree that reached higher than my second-story window. I was contemplating how one gathered the fruit that grew at tip top, when a little girl appeared with a long bamboo pole with a basket on the end. She extended the pole to the top of the tree, cupped the basket over a big, yellow papaya, jiggled it, and brought it down to the ground. A few minutes later, this child was knocking at our door. She presented us with this luscious tree-ripened papaya for our first breakfast in the Philippines.

I watched another drama in a house across the street. A house girl was polishing a mahogany floor. She had one half of a coconut husk under each foot, and thus shod she went skating gracefully over the floor. The oily husk gives a high gloss to the floors, which are polished each day. It is called " coconuting" the floors. The way the house boys and girls can skim over the floor on these husks is a form of art. They can do a native dance and polish the floor at the same time.

Morning broke over the tops of the huge old acacia trees. Never had I seen such beauty. I knew in that moment that every hardship, every danger (and there were to be many) that I was to endure within the next five years in the islands, were paid for in advance. Never had I seen such a glorious sunrise; it, too, was throwing out a welcome. It did not seem possible that this fresh, pink morning would soon lapse into a day so intense, so bright, so hot, that I could not smell the fragrance of the flowers in the garden below. Within an hour, this relentless sun would stalk across the sky, driving man and beast to shelter; it would turn the rippling blue waves of Manila Bay into a murky pool. And when it had spent itself across the sky, wearied, it would fling out an apology for its day of torment. For, across the horizon it would spread out a great fan of red, gold, turquoise, and mauve—a magnificent sunset that would settle over Corregidor, and even the brooding Rock would wear a halo of colors. The waters of Manila Bay would turn blood red, and the sunken battleships would appear like mauve-colored ghosts riding the waves of a blood red sea.

The dramatic break of day faded. I walked out on the upper porch where the cook was preparing breakfast. Mrs. Respicio had loaned us her cook until we could find our own. The girl had three little clay stoves on a bench; these were fired with small faggots of wood. One stove held a small clay pot in which was steaming rice; on another sat a coffee pot; the third held the wok, a big Chinese skillet, in which bacon was sizzling. The bacon had come out of a can. We were to live out of tin cans for our stay in the islands: powdered milk, powdered eggs, and rancid butter from Australia, the after-taste of which shall remain with me till my dying day.

The sleepy-headed family arose after the cook had heated and reheated breakfast a number of times. We were served a native bread the girl had bought at the sari-sari, the little store nearby. It is a heavy, sweetish-like dough and a very good bread, so the cook told us. For, she said, when you broke open this loaf of bread, the weevils were dead and you could pick them out before you ate it. Now, at the Chinaman's shop down the street, she informed us, they made larger loaves and baked them with such rapidity, when you broke open the loaves, the weevils, not yet dead, would crawl into your plates and get all mixed up with the powdered eggs. We learned to accept the weevil as part of our daily diet. I shall always believe they were wiggling vitamins, for we grew disgustingly healthy.

My very first day in the Philippines I hired a little house boy, fourteen-year-old José, lovable, ragged, and hungry. We took him shopping down at the Pasay market and bought him khaki shorts, sweatshirts, tennis shoes, and a haircut. He was proud as Punch. José could do many things: skim across the floor on a coconut, wash dishes, cook, make beds, clean "Adam." He proved to be a very honest lad and became a part of our household.

In the islands, you usually hire one person for each task: a houseboy, a cook, a housegirl and lavandera, and a driver for the car. That is the minimum number with which to run a household of three. You may hire more; that would depend on your husband's rank. The price the Americans paid for help was set by the Army. That is, a slip was sent around to all government personnel stating the wage scale to pay for various duties. You did not have to abide by it; it was merely a yardstick. However, when I started out housekeeping my help consisted of only two people.

Each day life in the Philippines presents new problems, and they are different from the problems we face in America—even to the small matter of buying a loaf of bread. One day, when José

and the part-time cook were busy, I grabbed my large hat, a sali-
cut, and headed for the little sari-sari, to buy a loaf of bread. A
sari-sari is a little store to accommodate the very poor who cannot
afford to buy a whole pound of sugar. At the sari-sari they may
buy a cup of sugar or vinegar, and perhaps just two cigarettes out
of a pack. Huddy asked José to go to the sari-sari, but José was
such a slowpoke, I said in my best Filipino lingo, "I will be the
one to go." Besides, I needed the exercise involved, for to reach
the sari-sari, I must strictly follow the path which was the street,
do a broad jump over four open sewer ditches, and climb over
three large concrete dumps of rubble, buildings destroyed by the
bombs. I must side-step the grassy spots, for there was always
danger of a demolition bomb "at ease." Almost every day we
read in the paper of a death due to bomb explosion.

When I reached the sari-sari, I discovered another ditch, a
sort of moat over which I would need to do another broad jump.
I poised, judging my distance so as not to leap through the
glass counter. And I made it. The pretty Filipina girl who kept
the establishment (and this was the one, incidentally, where you
bought bread with dead weevils), unaccustomed to such an All-
American entrance, glowered at me. When I pointed my finger at
a nice loaf of native bread, she made no effort to remove it from
the showcase. Rather, she asked disdainfully: "Have you no
houseboy?"

"Yes. I have a houseboy."

"Then why do *you* buy the bread?"

I knew I had lost face. Nevertheless, I made my purchase and
proceeded to leap over the ditch and start toward my house.
Then I got a sort of funny feeling inside me. I realized for the
first time in my life I felt ashamed to be carrying a loaf of bread.
Back in the States, I would have skipped down the street carefully holding the fresh loaf so as not to squash it. Had I met Mrs.
Smith, I would have opened the bag and let her sniff the good
odor of the bread so she might buy a loaf for her family. But in

the Philippines that loaf of bread became an undesirable parcel
that I shifted from my right hand to my left and back again. I
tried holding the loaf of bread behind me, in front of me, and at
last thrust it under my arm and flattened it like a pancake in my
effort to conceal it. Just as I had gained enough confidence to
continue up the street, I sighted Mrs. Respicio, my landlady, approaching, with her houseboy lagging six paces behind her carrying the family shopping bag.

Realizing that I had lost face, I had a sudden desire to turn
and run. But Mrs. Respicio had seen me, so I had to meet her
face to face (even though I had already lost mine). But what
should I do with my loaf of bread? I considered tossing it over
a high wall, or ducking it in an open sewer, or should I thrust it
into the hands of an old man who was approaching? I did none
of these things, because Mrs. Respicio, sensing my predicament,
very graciously relieved me of the flattened loaf of bread. She
handed it to her houseboy. He would deliver it to my house in
less time than I could say scat.

Huddy, disgusted that I should become so involved over a
mere loaf of bread, grabbed his cap. *He* would go to that sari-
sari and *he* would buy a loaf of bread. Just watch him! And I
did. In due time he returned empty-handed. He had encountered
a similar experience with Mrs. Reyes, our good neighbor across
the street. She had taken the loaf of bread which he had tucked
under his arm in his effort to conceal it, and *her* houseboy would
deliver it to our house in less time than he could say scat.

We didn't realize it took so long to say scat in the Philippines.
We waited and waited; still no bread. Huddy called José and
instructed him to accompany me to the sari-sari; he was to walk
six paces behind me carrying the shopping bag. That was the
way one went to market in the Philippines.

Once out of sight, I hustled José right up beside me, for it was
now getting dark. Besides, I wanted that girl at the bread
counter to know that I had both a houseboy and a face. I'd show

her! I might have made it, had we not met Mrs. Respicio who was returning. Poor José, realizing that he should be six paces in the rear, became so confused he started backing to assume proper position. He was not watching his step so he cut his foot badly on a piece of broken glass.

Mrs. Respicio accompanied me to a doctor's office to have the foot dressed. I sent José home in a jeepney and again started for the sari-sari, but it was closed. I returned home empty-handed but found my husband seated at the table staring wolfishly at two badly squashed loaves of bread. They had been delivered by the houseboys of our good neighbors.

"We've both lost face," he stormed. "We have simply got to hire a bread-totin' boy. That's the way one does it in the Philippines." I was so hungry that I agreed with him.

When morning came, I had worked out my own philosophy. I would not hire a bread-toting boy just because Mrs. Reyes had one. I would be myself in the Philippines, and would continue my American ways, so long as they did not infringe upon the rights of my neighbors. When Mrs. Respicio took my loaf of bread, she was being *herself*. She showed the bigness of her heart and her willingness to reach out a hand and help her neighbor— an American.

Chapter Three

IT WOULD BE several months before the government quarters were finished, so we started looking for another place to live. We were sorry to leave Mrs. Respicio, but the two small rooms were not adequate for three people. Very fortunately we found a brand-new house, painted white with green shutters. Bougainvillea climbed over the lattice and reached upstairs to the bedroom window. Lacy cadeña de amor grew at the windows and the pink blossoms tried vainly to hide the ugly iron bars to make us feel less as if we were living in a jail. All the windows were barred; no one would dare live in a house unless they had such protection. One window upstairs had the iron bars padlocked, with the key hanging on a nail beside the window. In case of fire, this was our only means of escape. We made sure the key was always in place.

There was a large sala, or living room, a tiny kitchen, two upstairs bedrooms, and a bath with a tub. A bathroom was indeed a luxury in war-torn Manila. This tub was made of brick, and when it was filled, you had to bathe like fury before the water seeped out between the cracks in the brick. Our furniture was composed of broken-down army items. We glamorized the old hospital beds by painting them a Chinese red and tinting the mosquito tents the same color. These long-legged beds painted red reminded me of flamingos. We were grateful the height of the hospital beds brought us up level with the windows, so the cool breeze from the Bay kissed our cheeks. On the other hand, these high beds had disadvantages. We lived in the Pasay district, a vulnerable spot, for Japs were still hiding in the outskirts; they didn't know the war was over. The Philippine Constabulary would go out at night with machine guns to try to rout them. The bullets would whiz over the top of our little house, and we dragged our mattresses off the beds to the floor to escape the line of fire.

Our little house was in a compound enclosed by a high iron fence with a gate that was padlocked day and night. The owner lived in the compound, and underneath his big house were quarters for several Filipino families. The back yard was the gathering place for the servants. The lavandera squatted under the mango tree to do the laundry in a little tub with a fluted rim not over six inches high. She washed the clothes in cold water, using her hands, or a little paddle to rid the garments of dirt. She would spread the clothes on the green grass to bleach, then rewash them, and they would come out amazingly white. The houseboy sat under the mango tree to shine shoes; the cook prepared vegetables; the driver sat in the car, ready to drive his mistress at her bidding. There were often more servants in a household than members of a family.

I continued to be a rebel. I refused to hire five servants to take care of three people. We had José, our bread-toting boy, and Belén, the lavandera who also helped with the housework and the cooking. We were still trying to find a cook, but so far had not been able to locate one. When Belén was too busy with other work, I rolled up my sleeves and asked José to teach me to fire the little native stove so I could cook bacon and eggs. We had an electric hot plate but the current was off more times than it was on. In the evening we usually ate at the Army and Navy Club.

José was such a happy boy; he was my right-hand pal. I shall never forget one day when we went to the Pasay market to buy a native stove. It seemed I had mishandled one of the little clay stoves and it had cracked. One handles a little stove very gently, I learned. You don't bang it against the bench under the mango tree.

Huddy remained in "Adam" while I started for the market with José walking six paces behind me. I made my purchase and returned in the same manner with José walking as straight as an arrow with the stove balanced on his head. We found Huddy sitting on the sidewalk with a small boy shining his shoes. This angered José. "Mom," said he, "I shine shoes very well. I shined the shoes for the officers at Clark Field."

Right away we drove José to the Army PX and Huddy let him select a good shoe shine kit. Afterwards, we had shiny shoes; even the old leather straps on "Adam" were as polished as an officer's boots.

José placed the little stove under the big mango tree in the back yard. That night when he went out to inspect it, he saw the chickens were roosting right over it. "Mom," he said, "I take the new stove in the house tonight, so the chickens won't step on it."

José loved to cook. Usually he burned the rice, and the bacon was too rare, but he could glorify a bean. On Saturdays we went sightseeing, so this was lima bean day. José would fill the little clay pot with beans and ham, then fire up the stove and sit over it all day long, feeding it faggots of wood just at the right time to keep an even temperature. Each lima bean was a mealy morsel with the skin just bursting and the ham deliciously tender.

My landlady told me about an excellent cook who lived in Angeles. However, there was a five-hundred peso debt against the girl that I would have to pay off, before I could hire her. So I continued to help with the cooking. Huddy was embarrassed that I should be in the kitchen. And the landlady was sure I had lost face.

In those days, in the islands, many families had servants

working off debts acquired years before by their fathers. My landlady had six servants. I am sure she paid them very little, yet she required long, back-breaking hours of work. The lavandera was required to starch and iron the bed sheets until not a wrinkle showed. This kept her busy so she didn't have time to sit down; the houseboy coconuted the floors twice a day. All her servants slept on mats on the garage floor and lived on rice and tidbits of fish. They were not permitted to sit down when they ate.

I like to think my landlady was an exception, and that others were not so cruel. One day she came over to give me instructions on how to treat my servants. I should not give José oranges and cookies. It would spoil him and make her servants dissatisfied. This visit was prompted by the fact that José had been dividing his goodies with Niño, her houseboy.

José told me that Niño was a slave. He was eighteen years old but could neither read nor write. His father had owed one thousand pesos at the time of his death. The family had taken Niño to work off the debt. Niño received five pesos per month which was applied on the debt. At this rate, it would take him almost seventeen years to square it. That is, if he didn't break a dish; in such case the price of the cup or plate was deducted from his salary. Many times he broke five pesos worth of dishes in one month, for the landlady screamed at him so much he dropped many dishes.

Despite hardships, Niño had a happy disposition. He sat under the big mango tree and shined shoes for the family, and sang as he worked. At night, when the chores were done, he would stand under the stars and sing. I used to watch him from my bedroom window. He stood erect with his chest out, living the song he sang, using gestures as if he were a star on a stage. Suddenly the concert ended, for the landlady would scream at him to stop the noise and get to bed. He would walk slowly toward the garage, still humming softly as if he must finish the song he had started. Then all was quiet, and I knew that Niño had flopped on his dirty mat—perhaps to dream.

Each morning Niño would help the landlady's two young daughters and son off to school. He would carry their books to the car and assist them into the vehicle, then unlock the gate for the driver. There was a look of yearning on his face as he watched them drive away. José would watch him, then say: "Mom, Niño would like so much to go to school."

Niño was a handsome boy, far more handsome than the young master he served. He had a right to an education. Yet a debt of one thousand pesos would keep him a slave for many years. Was there no hope? He had a beautiful voice, yet no one cared enough to help him, or to encourage him. The landlady whom he served was reported to be very wealthy. Why couldn't she wipe out this debt and free him? Often I wondered if there were any way I might help this boy. I, too, dreamed of Niño on a stage singing his heart out. Then the sharp clapping of the landlady's hands, as she summoned her slave, would bring me back to earth.

One day José was polishing our shoes under the mango tree. Niño watched him for a minute, then slipped his feet into a pair of Huddy's shoes and strutted around like a peacock. The shoes fitted him. I grabbed a pair of socks and walked out toward the mango tree. When Niño saw me coming, he was so frightened that he quickly stepped out of the shoes.

"Niño, don't remove them," I said, as I handed him the socks. "I'm going to give them to you."

He told me he had no money, but José assured him I was a very kind "mom" and that he didn't need to pay for them. He was very appreciative and slipped away to the garage to hide the shoes in an old bamboo crate so the landlady would not find them. He had never owned a pair of shoes before. That night Niño ran away, wearing his new shoes. José said he had scaled the high iron fence at midnight. I wondered if José hadn't given him a boost, for the fence was very high. Anyway, José and I kept very quiet. All day, the entire household was astir, for it appeared their one thousand peso debt was going, going, gone!

Two days later the master came driving back with Niño in his car. He had located him in his hometown province strutting around in a pair of officer's shoes. I felt so sorry for Niño when the shoes were taken from him. He also lost the five peso monthly salary for three months and was given extra heavy duties to perform. Yet, that night he again stood under the mango tree and sang his heart out—until he was silenced.

José could neither read nor write for during the war and the Japanese Occupation, he, like other Filipino children, was running from barrio to barrio in search of food and to escape the enemy. It was a matter of survival. There were no schools. Harvel became deeply concerned over José's plight and decided to start a little school in the back yard under the big mango tree. She would teach a couple of hours each afternoon when the servants were not busy with household chores. Her father secured a small blackboard from army surplus and a supply of paper and pencils.

Harvel and José set up the school room right beside Belén's washtub. The blackboard was hung on the mango tree but each night José carried it inside the house to protect it. José rounded up the youngsters across the way who lived in the shabby huts called barong-barongs. He supplied them with tablets and pencils to prove this was to be a real school and it was free. And the teacher was very pretty.

Four little boys aged seven to nine appeared the next afternoon with pencils and tablets ready for school. They wore not one stitch of clothes and were completely unashamed of their nakedness. Harvel knew she must maintain order and dignity so she sent them home. They could return on the morrow if they came with clothes on. She stressed the fact they should wear three items of clothing. José translated the instructions in Tagalog and Harvel held up three fingers to make sure they understood. The little boys held up three fingers. Yes, they understood.

The next day José rang the little school bell to summon the pupils. The little boys came running, all smiles, for they had done exactly what teacher had told them to do. They each wore three items of clothing: a string of shell beads, tennis shoes, and an old army helmet!

Harvel was at her wits' end. But José solved the problem. He slipped into the kitchen and appropriated four of my large tea towels. He tried to dress the boys in G-strings, but the big squares wouldn't make a G-string wrap, so he ended up by diapering the four boys. And school commenced. When Huddy arrived home, he was so amused that after school, he and José loaded the youngsters into "Adam" and they drove to Pasay market. He bought khaki shorts and sweat shirts to outfit all of them.

José was an apt pupil and learned to write his name quickly. He was so proud of this accomplishment, that everything he owned bore big box-car letters "JOSE." Niño would stand at a distance and absorb everything Harvel wrote on the blackboard. José whispered to me, "Niño would like to go to our school." Harvel invited him to join them even though he was much older. She was amazed at Niño's intelligence. He had a flair for numbers and learned to add very quickly. This annoyed the landlady as she stood at her window and watched the progress of the little school. She must put a stop to it. She would not have Niño learning arithmetic, for this knowledge would inevitably undermine the system of bookkeeping by which Niño was indebted to her. So she marched right over to Harvel and informed her she might teach reading and writing, but she would not allow her to teach arithmetic in her back yard.

Very well, then they would use this time to learn to sing. José wanted to learn a song about the American Flag, "A Star

Sprinkly Banner." Harvel interpreted his wish. It was "The Star
Spangled Banner." She wrote the title on the blackboard and
they learned to pronounce the name of the song. She stood in
front of the little group and repeated: "Oh, say can you see by
the dawn's early light." Now all together, one line at a time . . .
"Oh, say can you see!" She repeated it again and again. Hands
went up. Yes, they had it. With gusto, they sang out: "José,
canyuh see."

In desperation I went to an agency to try to find a cook. That
afternoon a girl was sent to my house: a very pretty girl, with her
dark hair piled neatly on top of her head, who, in her uniform,
resembled more a clinical nurse. She slipped her feet out of her
bakyas, or sandals, and entered the house barefooted. I immediately made up my mind—she was too pretty to make a good
cook. She must have read my thoughts, for she pleaded, "Oh
Mom, please just give me a chance." The hurt look in her eyes and
the tear in her voice won my heart. I was never to regret my
decision. And from this little servant girl, I was to learn a great
lesson: that one could be beaten down to earth and could rise
again, chin up.

Her name was Josefina but she preferred to be called Josie.
She had been enslaved by the Japanese, and had been beaten
and slapped when she had resented cleaning up their "hogpen"
rooms. To humiliate a Filipina girl who refused to serve as a
mistress, a Jap would use the middle of the floor to deposit his
stool when the bathroom was not ten feet away.

For days Josie would jump and scream at the sound of even
Huddy's footsteps, or at the sound of any man's voice, for she
was still in a state of shock. She was pitifully undernourished
and had no clothes except the borrowed uniform she was wearing. We bought her new clothes and she seemed to gain confidence and to feel she belonged with us. She wanted to live in,
but we had no servants' quarters. I went over to try to rent a

garage room from the landlady. Right away she brought over a dirty mat and said that Josie should sleep on the kitchen floor, then by four o'clock in the morning her bones would be aching and she'd be willing to get up and get at her work.

There was a small airy hallway upstairs that we curtained off to make a tiny room for her. She had an army cot with clean linens, a table, and a chair. She had finished the sixth grade at school, and was an avid reader. We furnished her with magazines and books, and in her spare time she read and studied. She would write down the words she didn't understand and would ask us about them the next morning.

When the landlady saw Josie's room, she reminded me that I would lose face by indulging a servant with such luxury. She said that even Josie would lose respect for me.

However, Josie blossomed like a native orchid. She learned to trust us and we knew we could trust her. She did the marketing, handled the grocery money, and always accounted for every penny she spent. When I went to the army commissary, I naturally bought steak and pork chops for all of us. I have heard American women say their servants would eat only fish and rice. That is a mistaken idea, for they liked other food too. There were those who said we indulged our servants. At least we never put a padlock on our ice box as I regret to say many Americans did.

And what an ice box! It could far outshine Betty MacDonald's stove in *The Egg and I.* It was a coal-oil burning ice box from Australia that had been used in the hospitals. All refrigerators used in the war area were of the oil-burning type. This old number, a double unit, had two flat kerosene pans that slid underneath, and each was topped with a little lamp with a wick and a globe. The wicks had burned so short they would not reach the oil pan; and new wicks had to come from Australia. I pinned a piece of muslin onto the wick, but the old box would send up puffs of smoke like a steam engine. The walls of the house would be covered with soot, our clothes smudged, and the food spoiled. I would find Josie under the old box as black as a chimney sweep, with tears streaming down her face. "Mom, it is just an old devil!" Harvel and I christened the temperamental old box "Old Diablo." We painted it a Chinese red and Harvel sketched a big black devil holding a pitchfork on the door, and underneath I inscribed: "Old Diablo." It became a conversation piece in our house.

One day I crawled under "Old Diablo" and by some twist I learned just how to adjust the wick, but I couldn't teach Josie or José how it was done. I was to be the one to baby-sit with "Old Diablo" until the electric boxes arrived from the States. Many times when friends dropped by and asked if I were at home, Huddy would say: "Yes, she's under the ice box." And for one year, I practically lived under the thing. When we went out in the evenings, most likely when I returned there would be a note from Josie on my pillow: "Mom, get under the ice box please."

The weeks spent under "Old Diablo" began to tell on me. I was always covered with soot and smelled of kerosene. In fact, before Josie dared let me take off to a cocktail party, she would be at the front door to sniff me. If I smelled too strongly of kerosene, she would go out in the garden and pick gardenias and pin them in my hair. She believed the heavy perfume of the gardenias mingled with the kerosene would fool my friends. They would think it was some rare perfume from India.

Evidently Josie gave up hopes that the new electric boxes would ever arrive. She was afraid the long siege with "Old Diablo" would make me an old woman before my time. One day she came from market with a large yellow fruit. It was "the fruit of perpetual life." The Philippine people attributed longevity to the eating of this fruit, and any girl who ate it would remain forever young and beautiful.

The "jack fruit," or durian, grows on a tree and is hauled in by bull cart and piled in the markets, as we might pile up watermelons. It is about the size of a big round melon, but the outer skin is so tough you have to whack it open with a hand axe. The odor is so obnoxious that should you close your eyes, you would swear you were inside the stockyards at Ft. Worth, Texas.

Nevertheless, Josie was going to feed me this mystic and magical fruit for she wanted me to remain young and beautiful. Each day, at three o'clock, we set aside the time for my "jack fruit" tea. I would close my eyes and hold my nose while I tried to eat the sticky white stuff that tasted for all the world like rotten eggs. Each day became agony. Castor oil I would have relished, but not this everlasting fruit! Finally I grew faint at the thought of it and when the hour of three rolled around, I was in such a state of exhaustion that Josie had to spoon the stuff into my mouth.

I grew older instead of younger. Finally I rebelled, and at three o'clock each day, I would go crawl under "Old Diablo" and swear that it needed tampering with again.

Chapter Four

THE U.S. VETERAN'S ADMINISTRATION, Regional Office, was temporarily located at 635 Florento Torres St., a building occupied before the war by the *Manila Bulletin,* an American-owned newspaper. It was badly damaged by bombs. There was not a window pane in the building, and when typhoons hit, the open spaces were covered with pieces of rusty tin to protect the government files, records of the Filipino veterans waiting to be adjudicated. Later, the V.A. Regional Office was transferred to the Heacock Building on the Escolta and the *Manila Bulletin* resumed publication in its former location.

Doctor Huddleston was assigned to the Regional Office with the title Assistant Chief Medical Officer for the entire Archipelago. In this capacity he often traveled from southern Mindanao to northern Luzon to examine ailing veterans. I was permitted to travel with him (at my own expense) and learned to know and to love the Philippine people.

It was in the V.A. office that the doctor first met Ramón Magsaysay, the heroic leader of the guerrilla forces at Zambales, known to history as "Magsaysay's Guerrillas."

Doctor Huddleston believed, as did many others, that the guerrilla fighters really saved the Philippines. After the fall of Bataan, these brave men, both Filipinos and Americans, took to the hills and carried on a resistance campaign against the Japanese. Their slogan: "We Remained!" was an answer to the famous: "I Shall Return!" Without the help of the guerrilla fighters who refused to be enslaved by the Japanese, that famous promise might never have been fulfilled. If this had happened, the prestige of the United States would have suffered a blow in the Far East from which it might never have recovered.

Ramón Magsaysay firmly believed that General MacArthur would return and he inspired his little army to fight on. And that day came. On January 9, 1945, General MacArthur landed his invasion forces at Lingayen Gulf, and proceeded toward Manila.

It was a proud day for Captain Magsaysay when he told his weary fighters that victory was in sight. It was a sad-looking little army. The men were barefoot, hungry, and in rags. But they stood tall as General MacArthur passed by.

Did Ramón Magsaysay apologize for their appearance? He did not! He believed his little army was made up of the best and bravest men in the world, men who had gone through hell for over three years and would go through another three such years, if called upon, to free the Philippines.

It was to bring health and medical assistance to brave men such as these that my husband had gone to the Philippines. And this was to be his finest hour in medicine, and sadly to be his grand finale.

I shall never forget the day I met Ramón Magsaysay. Huddy had brought him to our house after office hours. This was one of the days "Old Diablo" blew his stack, sending out columns of smoke comparable to an eruption at Mt. Mayon. I had just emerged from under the ice box. Unable to find the trouble, I had started upstairs to the bathroom to clean up before Huddy's arrival. There I stood, in the middle of the sala, looking for all the world like a chimney sweep.

"This is Ramón Magsaysay," said Huddy. I looked at this husky man dressed in plain khaki trousers and a big flowered sport shirt. I'm sure I greeted him, but I only remember bursting into tears and screaming at Huddy: "Get that 'Old Diablo' out of my house!" Ramón stood aghast at my temper explosion and was actually backing out of the room, when Huddy assured him my wrath was directed only toward the ice box.

"Now let me take a look at that Old Devil," Ramón said. "I'm a pretty good mechanic." He went under "Old Diablo" and tinkered and tampered, then emerged. "It's working!" It took him less than three minutes and he wasn't even "smutty." It was all in knowing what to do. A few days later the ice box again refused to work, and Josie said: "Mom, call Mr. Magsaysay." I reminded Josie that Mr. Magsaysay was at the Legislative Building at work for he was serving as a Congressman from Zambales. He had no time to tinker with ice boxes.

It was Ramón Magsaysay who encouraged me to gather stories about his people each day. He said I should always carry a notebook with me to record sights and events of the reconstruction days in the Philippines for posterity. And it was this suggestion of his which led to my writing a regular column for the *Philippine Herald*.

I liked to go to Quiapo Market, to wander down Dasmariñas Street, or to ride to Chinatown in a calesa, a small two-wheeled buggy drawn by a pony with the driver sitting up front.

Such excursions caused Josie much concern. She briefed me again and again on the thousand and one things that might happen to me. I should never, never wear a wrist watch for it would be snatched from my arm, and before I reached the next corner, a vendor would be trying to sell it back to me. The street corner vendors usually wore some twenty or thirty wrist watches, bracelet fashion from wrist to elbow, and many a G.I. bought his own watch from these peddlers.

Nor should I give money to the beggars, even though an emaciated-looking woman with a starving child astraddle her hip always tore at my heart. Josie informed me this was just an act. There was an organization in Manila that hired beggars to go out and work on the sympathy of people. When night came, the poor woman with the baby would turn over her earnings to the big bosses. In turn, they would dole out a mere pittance to her. She had barely enough to buy a bowl of rice, while they waxed rich.

I must never sling my purse over my shoulder, lest a thief slip up behind me and cut the strap to make off with the purse and its contents. I must carry the purse tightly under the pit of my arm. I could be robbed right on a jeepney. The pickpockets were that slick.

The city bus service consisted of jeepneys which were glorified army jeeps that swarmed through the streets of Manila snarling up traffic. They were gay little vehicles that always reminded me of the surrey with the fringe on top. These remodeled army jeeps had a low-slung body like that of a pickup truck. The benches on which the passengers rode ran lengthwise. You entered at the rear; a barker took your twenty centavos fare and then you tried to find a seat. The passengers sat facing each other. In the tiny aisle were baskets of smelly dried fish, often squawking chickens in a coop, and once I sat with my feet on a bamboo cage that held a squealing pig. But oh, how I learned about life in Manila as I rode this oriental surrey with the fringe on the top!

I loved to read the names on the jeepneys: "God Is My Copilot"; "My Gal Sal"; "God Bless the Philippines"; and that famous, "I Shall Return."

I started out on my news beat with fifty pesos pinned in the upper pocket of my cotton blouse. That would stop the pickpockets! I had chosen my favorite jeepney, one painted Chinese red with a striped canopy, and across the panel under the windshield was painted: "Deep in the Heart of Texas." Since I am Texas-born, I always wanted to believe they fixed this one up just for me, even though they didn't know I was coming.

"Deep in the Heart of Texas" was stacked with people. I wedged myself between a very thin old woman whose hip bones jabbed at me; on the other side was a young man dressed in an immaculate sharkskin suit of deep pink. The old lady smoked a small cigar, hind part before. When she opened her mouth and started to put the lighted end inside, I was sure she couldn't see, so I grabbed her hand, "That is the wrong end; you'll burn the roof of your mouth!" The young man in the pink suit assured me that was the way to smoke the small black cigar. I was simply fascinated with her smoking; she sat contentedly for a long spell with the fire end of the cigar in her mouth, then removed it and puffed smoke like an engine. She snuffed out the lighted end and placed the cigar in her basket.

When we reached Quiapo Market, I hurried to The Yellow Lantern, to buy a piece of linen. I made my purchase and reached in my pocket for my fifty peso bill. It was not there. Even the button on the flap of my pocket had been neatly cut off. My pink-clad companion managed to snitch the money while we discussed the proper way to smoke a cigar.

Manila was seething with people. They didn't even try to stay on the sidewalks, but swelled out in the middle of the streets like great waves. The vendors set up their stalls right in the middle of Carriedo Street to carry on business. It was a street as colorful as a rainbow, as they flaunted yard goods to customers: silks from China and cottons from India. Many of these stalls were just an orange crate, and a vendor might have less than six pieces of goods to sell. They barked out their wares hoping to make enough money to buy a ganto measure of rice, about three pounds. Some sold tinned foods in gray cans—I knew they were Army Commissary cans, perhaps stolen—others sold surgical instruments, good stainless steel ones that also had belonged to the Army, hospital gowns, and bathrobes. And there were little rice birds in bamboo cages for sale for twenty centavos, and clusters of bright-colored balloons.

I paused to watch an aged woman as she squatted beside a stall, her little store which was a large rattan tray balanced on an old nail keg. I took note of the scantiness of her wares: three packages of chiclets, two packages of native peanuts, two baluts (native egg delicacies), three packages of American brand cigarettes, and three overripe bananas.

I watched her claw-like hands rearrange her wares; she placed the peanuts to the far side of the tray and moved the cigarettes up front. She would probably shift and reshift the items many times. At day's end, she would place her little store atop her head and walk slowly toward her barong-barong. Her home was likely just a piece of tin leaned up against a bombed-out building. She would eat a bowl of rice and one tiny dried fish, then stretch out on a hard mat to sleep. Tomorrow she would start all over again.

As I watched this scene, I became aware that someone, very near, was watching me. I remembered Josie warning: "Someday, Mom, you are going to be kidnapped and carried away to China and the doctor will have to ransom you home." I looked up and straight into the eyes of a bewhiskered Arab wearing a yellow turban, khaki shorts, and shirt which appeared to be army clothes that had been stripped of insignia. He carried a handsome brief case made of alligator skin. I had seen him before. In fact, every time I went to Quiapo Market, I had the feeling he was following me. If I stood on this corner, he was here; if I crossed over, he was there. Always watching me. I had not paid him much attention, except to hold tighter on to my purse. Today, I was afraid. I had no desire to be kidnapped and carried away by an Arab.

Cautiously I wandered on toward Rizal Avenue. Then I started to walk very fast, pushing through the crowd to escape him. I looked back and there he was right on my heels. Then I made double-quick time down the avenue and made sure he was not close enough to grab me and drag me inside some dive. Suddenly there didn't seem to be any sidewalk under me. I had the sensation I was treading water. And I was.

I had stepped into an open manhole on the sidewalk right in front of the Avenue Theatre. During the war, the Japanese had stolen all the iron covers, and the manholes were now covered with wooden lids. These covers were often taken during the night by the Filipinos who chopped them up for wood to kindle the small clay stoves. I had presence of mind enough to spread my arms eagle-like to keep from being sucked down into the manhole and far out into the China Sea. My purse went one way, my notebook another. Two Filipino boys standing at the theatre box office rushed over and lifted me out. I was dripping wet and smeared from head to foot with foul-smelling refuse from the sewer. My shoes, which were ballet flats, were gone, perhaps by this time half way to Shanghai.

The boys stretched me out on the sidewalk, right in front of the theatre. My left leg was bleeding badly, for my dimensions were slightly larger than the circumference of the manhole, and a portion of my left thigh and hip were badly bruised. I was in great pain and feared my leg might be broken. I had been taught by my husband that in such an event I should lie very, very still until help arrived. I asked one of the Filipino boys to phone my husband's office and ask him to come to me at once; also to call the Manila Police Department. I would take them to task for permitting an open manhole on the sidewalk. For, had a small child stepped into this opening, it would have disappeared and never been accounted for.

As I lay sprawled on the sidewalk waiting for my husband, a crowd of people gathered around me. In post-war days, telephone service was very poor, so the doctor's delay was to be expected. A half an hour went by, and now I was completely encircled by people and I was near suffocation. The pain in my leg was growing worse. The crowd shoved and pushed and at times almost fell over me. One of the Filipino boys who had helped rescue me stood over me and kept asking the crowd, in Tagalog, to move back. The crowd responded to his request. Suddenly, I saw two big brown legs encased in a pair of khaki shorts standing directly over me. I looked up into the eyes of the Arab.

I was frightened. Fearing he had come to claim "the body," even though at this stage with the refuse dried on my clothes I was completely deglamorized, I asked the Filipino boy to get out on Rizal Avenue and hail the first American soldier he saw and bring him to my side. Almost immediately the boy was back with two U.S. Army Captains. And never did a khaki uniform look so good to me.

The soldiers very gently lifted my bloody body and pack-saddle-wise were carrying me to an army jeep to transport me to the 13th Station Hospital when, all at once, bedlam broke loose. Down the street came a convoy of jeeps, led by the Chief of Police, sirens wide open. They took over, saying in good Filipino lingo: "We will be the ones to take her." The army captains placed me in the lead jeep. I never saw the Arab again.

The police jeeps, followed by the army jeep, sped down Rizal Avenue with sirens wide open. A great throng of people lined the streets, no doubt believing I had just robbed a Manila bank.

The doctor hurried out to the 13th Station Hospital to take care of me. The nurses stripped me of my clothes. I remember they were holding up my suit with a pair of forceps. It was so nasty they dared not touch it. "Burn it," the doctor yelled out. And it was my good brown linen I had bought in San Francisco!

Very fortunately my leg was not broken, but I was given tetanus and other shots as a safeguard. For many weeks, my left leg was as black as tar and was swollen to twice its normal size. I was very lame and had to be assisted up and down steps. I had embarrassing moments, for Huddy was forever making me "Exhibit No. 1." This exposé usually happened on the terrace of the Army and Navy Club when other doctors had gathered. But with fifteen doctors on my case, my leg remained the color of a stove pipe. I became very popular, for the minute I entered the Army and Navy Club, I had a dozen men rush forward to assist me up and down steps. I always had at least a colonel on each arm, and sometimes even drew a general.

The other women at the Club became very envious. Some of them even considered scouting around for an open manhole through which *they* might plunge.

One day I discovered I no longer was a solo member of my Calamity Club. Doris Baldwin, who was en route to the islands to join her husband on duty in Manila, stopped over in Honolulu. Doris was walking along the pier, gazing toward Diamond Head, when she walked off the pier and was floundering in water that was ink-black with oil from the ships. She was fished ashore and it took the rest of the day to clean her up. I made her a member of my club. Then Ann Bartl soon qualified for membership. We were on a small army boat picnicking on deck within sight of Bataan's white beaches. The good swimmers had dived in and were headed toward Bataan. Ann was so engrossed in watching the race, she fell overboard. We had to work like fury to retrieve her for what seemed the jaws of a man-eating shark. Afer we pulled her back on deck, we found it was only a playful porpoise that was spanking her with its tail!

This Calamity Club luckily never had more than the three of us as members. And to date no one has yet outranked me. I am still president.

Chapter Five

THE UNIVERSITY OF THE PHILIPPINES re-opened its doors the first week in December, 1946, for the first time in four years. Before the war, this school with an enrollment of 10,000 was considered one of the most beautiful universities in the world. Now it stood in utter ruin. The outside walls, once snow white, now darkened from the smoke of battle, were shell-pocked. The crumbling walls leaned precariously, with pieces of twisted and warped steel that flanged out like the over-sized tentacles of an octopus. There was not a window pane in the building. The openings were nailed up with pieces of rusty tin. Amid this destruction the bougainvillea flourished, the luxuriant blossoms falling over the gaunt ugliness of the building like a magnificent purple waterfall.

The front steps of the Administration Building were bombed out. Harvel and I made our entrance by walking a long shaky plank. Students milled in the dark corridors, trying to read the bulletin board and waiting their turn to register. When we inquired about the office of Dr. Gonzales, the president, a Filipino boy very kindly escorted us to him.

Dr. Gonzales, dressed in an immaculate white linen suit, was seated at an old three-legged desk, the fourth leg being a small oil barrel rescued from a rubbage heap. He arose and extended his hand most cordially. He offered no apologies; rather with pride he told us how he had been able to salvage a few of the

59

buildings to re-open the university. The staff of teachers included Filipinos who had been educated in the States and associated with the school before the war. Their salary was one hundred pesos per month (fifty American dollars). Other staff members were wives of Army and Navy personnel who would give of their time gratuitously. Right away he asked me if I could help out in the English Department. I had to decline since I had already promised to head the Department of Journalism and Publications in the American School.

As we talked to Dr. Gonzales, I had the feeling that Harvel was not happy with the surroundings. Was she comparing the University of the Philippines with the University of Texas where she had completed her freshman year—a university so rich that it was campused by girls in mink coats and boys in bench-made boots driving custom-built Cadillacs? I ventured to suggest that she enroll in Santo Tomas, the university used as the internment camp for Americans during the war, and which was not bombed.

Harvel answered immediately: "I'm sure I shall be very happy here." And she enrolled, the only American student, and cast her lot with three thousand boys and girls, most of them from the Philippines.

These were pioneer days in the Orient, comparable to our Little Red School House days, for the students sat on boxes, on benches, and the teacher's desk was a rough board held up by two oil barrels. There were no books, except mimeographed copies, for all books had been burned by the Japanese who had used the buildings during The Occupation. The monsoon rains came through the big holes in the walls and often drenched the students.

It was a challenge. Harvel, for the very first time in her life, had to burn the midnight oil to hold her own, for her classmates were devoted students. She entered into the spirit of the school, worked on the college paper, took part in the school plays and in other activities. Her association with the students at the University of the Philippines, no doubt, will always be remembered by her as one of the finest interludes in her school life.

Contrary to the advice given us by the ugly American on the plane, we opened our home to Harvel's classmates. The girls were beautifully mannered, so artistic and with such a zest for living. It was a joy and a privilege to entertain them.

The Filipino boys also took a fancy to their American classmate. They didn't wait for an invitation but would arrive at our little white house by jeep-load, bearing leis of sweet sampaguita, a tiny white flower, to string around Harvel's neck. And she loved it. This avalanche of boys came just at our dinner hour, six o'clock. The Filipinos usually dine at eight or later; however, they have merianda, afternoon tea, at around four o'clock. So the boys, finishing this hour of refreshment, were out for a lark.

They would never dine with us, so Josie was forced to heat and reheat the food many times, until the stroke of eight. At this hour they would dash away.

Harvel's favorite classmate was Doy Laurel, son of José P. Laurel. During The Occupation, Doy's father served as the Japanese-appointed President of the Philippines. He was accused of being a collaborator, yet he had done the best he could to serve the Philippine people under the tyranny of the enemy. Doy often spoke of these days as he visited in our home. "My father loved his country and his people." He was always deeply touched when he spoke of those days. "My father often had to speak words the Japs put into his mouth with a bayonet at his back."

His father was under heavy fire during the Roxas administration, and because fingers pointed at him, the collaborator, we were severely criticized by some of our American friends for entertaining his son.

Doy had asked Harvel to go to a dance at Malacañang Palace. It was their first date. Harvel was so excited. She had chosen the evening gown she would wear, but she had neither cologne nor perfume. In our great haste to take passage on the "Sacred Carabao" for Manila, she had forgotten her perfume in a San Francisco hotel room. We simply had to find a bottle of perfume.

We searched through the Army PX. They had shaving lotion, shampoo, and a bottle of turpentine. No perfume. Finally we went to Botica Boie, the only drug store on the Escolta which was open for business. The Escolta, once the Fifth Avenue of Manila, was now a heap of rubble. We climbed over great mounds of concrete and crawled under tall buildings toppled over in the street to reach this botica which was housed under pieces of tin. We made our way through the dark aisles to the cosmetic counter and found a small bottle of Cashmere Bouquet toilet water, a size that would probably sell for fifteen cents at a Woolworth store. It was priced eighteen pesos. Nine good American dollars. A luxury. But we bought it. After all, it was for quite an occasion and Harvel was seventeen.

Doy arrived in his father's limousine with a bodyguard. Since he was the son of the ex-president, he traveled in style.

The next day he came over with a tiny black kitten, a cross between a Siamese and a black panther, which he presented to Harvel. It's name was JoJo. And what a cat he turned out to be! Sleek, streamlined, and when full-grown, he measured forty inches from head to tip of tail. We grew very fond of JoJo.

Harvel and Doy were taking a course in biology and spent many hours looking for frogs to dissect. One day Doy came into the house, picked up JoJo and started out of the door. "I'm sorry to take the cat," he looked at me with a poker face. "But we could not catch a frog and we simply must have a project to work on tomorrow. JoJo will do!"

I flew at him in a rage, only to find he was teasing me. He placed the kitten very tenderly in my arms.

While Harvel and Doy were busy at the University, I was busy at the American School, Inc. on Taft Avenue. This school, one of the finest in the Orient, was established many years ago to accommodate the children of the Army and Navy and other American personnel as well as children from many foreign lands.

The American School had also been occupied by the Japanese. The teachers rolled up their sleeves, and with shovels, dug out the dirt, so school could open. I spent three hours each morning at this school, trying to reorganize and get going with the publications, the school paper, the school annual, and all publicity. What a challenge! I also took over as head of the Journalism Department. The journalism room had not a single desk or a typewriter. The students and I sat on the floor with our pencils and scratch pads. And in this manner we put out the first issue of *The Bamboo Telegraph,* a school paper which not only represented the school, but the American Colony as well. Our first issue, a six page paper printed by the Ramon Roces Publications, set a standard. From then on, come rain, earthquake, or typhoon, the paper came out on time.

I went to the army and begged for desks, typewriters, and chairs. I got them on a memorandum sheet. Soon we had a journalism room that we were proud of. *The Bamboo Telegraph* became a popular weekly and at the end of nine months was entered in the Columbia Scholastic Press Association, Columbia University, New York, along with every school paper in the States. We were a proud group when we learned we had won high honors for the American School in far away Manila.

There were exciting moments. For instance, in 1948, when Governor Dewey of New York ran on the Republican ticket against President Truman for the office of Chief Executive of our nation, we were certain, due to the wire services information, that Dewey was the winner. So certain were we, that we had the front page of *The Bamboo Telegraph* made up with stories about the Deweys and their family in the White House, with a nice picture of them and their two children on the front page. It was election night in the United States, so we stayed with our paper down at the Ramon Roces plant until four o'clock in the morning. To our surprise, over the wire service came the news that Truman was leading the ticket, and by daylight Dewey had conceded. The front page of our paper was killed. We worked feverishly to get out a new page and a picture of the President. We dispatched Jerry Davis, our editor, to the American Embassy to find a good picture of him. He returned with one of President Truman cutting a birthday cake, the only one available. The president wore a big grin and had his right hand in mid air holding a knife ready to cut the cake. To make the picture fit a three column space, we cut off the cake. That left a grinning Truman with an uplifted knife. Our headline read: "PRESIDENT TRUMAN SLASHES THROUGH TO VICTORY!" And *The Bamboo Telegraph* rolled off the presses.

The hours spent in the American School, even though they deprived me of many precious moments when I should have been gathering news for one of my columns, were one of the highpoints of my stay in the Philippines. I had the feeling that I was helping in a small way to rebuild this school.

The American School was the center of education for American students on the Archipelago who were thousands of miles from their homeland. The school flew the American Flag, but even so, boys and girls from many lands passed through its doors and shared with the Americans the best in education. The school was a symbol of education; the center of international culture for the mingling of youth from twelve different countries and former students from various other lands who were now stateless. And with this mingling came a development of minds, personalities, and exchange of ideas and ways of life—tolerance, human understanding, and a love for all mankind.

Our first sight-seeing trip was up Tagaytay Road, one of the most beautiful drives around Manila. We jogged along in "Adam" and for miles and miles passed through little barrios, unable to tell where one ended and another began. The nipa huts hugged the highway so close that, should we meet a car, we had to maneuver the jeep so as not to hit an aged man sitting on the door step. The huts were built exactly alike with potted plants and fern in the window, and flowering bougainvillea over the doorway. Even the family washing on the clothes-lines seemed to have identical garments of red, blue, yellow, and green fluttering in the breeze.

The barrio scenes were picturesque. We met a cart loaded with green coconuts drawn by an old carabao, or water buffalo, and on the animal's broad back a little boy fast asleep. Other wooden-wheeled carts were loaded with chickens in bamboo crates, or with squealing pigs in baskets.

The market stalls were filled with fresh vegetables, dried fish, and baskets for rice. Women wearing large hats walked along the street carrying baskets of vegetables and fish, others balanced baskets on their heads. A group of women wearing beautifully embroidered blouses and wrap-around skirts of gay-colored plaids, were on their way to church. They wore black lace prayer veils and carried rosaries in their hands.

After we left the barrio section, we entered a country lane bordered with flowering white bud trees. And here, too, we came upon the rice fields with the harvest in full sway. It was a windy day and the women were winnowing rice, for this task is done on such a day. They wore red skirts and pieces of red cloth, draped veil-like over big hats. Each woman carried a big bamboo tray. A trio of young men, one with a guitar, strolled around the large mounds of rice, singing. To the melody of their tune, the women lifted the bamboo trays high above their heads, in sort of a pantomime, and the golden grains poured to the earth as the brisk wind fanned away the husks. This rice winnowing is a very solemn occasion, like a prayer.

Small rice stacks, round and firm and brown, like the full breasts of a young girl, dotted the golden-stubbled fields. On top of each was a white cross around which fluttered a covey of little

rice birds. In an irrigation ditch at the edge of the field a herd
of carabaos was submerged with only eyes and horns visible. This
animal's thick, non-porous hide, necessitates a daily bath so he
can survive the heat. One carabao, fresh from his bath, stood
chewing his cud, and a flock of little rice birds fluttered around
and settled on his back. It was a beautiful and peaceful sight.

We left the rice fields to enter a dense coconut grove. The
tall trees reached skyward for a breath of air, or for warmth of
sunlight. The ground underneath was dank, and beautiful ferns
grew around the roots of the trees. I could hear the raspy rustling
of the fronds, and there was an occasional thud as a coconut
dropped to the ground, split open, and spilled the delicious
milk. Squatted along the roadside were small boys with piles of
coconuts for sale, usually five for one peso.

We left the coconut grove and came to green rolling hills,
covered with papaya trees which bear the world's most delicious
fruit. Here, too, were patches of pineapples. However, in this
locality the pineapples are not too good for eating and are grown
only for their fiber, which is made into sheer, silky pina cloth, a
material that lends itself to beautiful embroidery work. On the
other hand, on the island of Mindanao, the Del Monte Farms
cultivate a pineapple for canning that is the sweetest and the
juiciest I have ever tasted.

Tagaytay Ridge is one of the beauty spots of the Philippines.
We drove "Adam" right up to Inspiration Point and had barely
stopped when Filipino boys came running to sell us their produce.
At least a dozen were on my side of the jeep and as many more
on the other side. Bunches of bananas were shoved in my face:
"Buy from me, Mom," a dozen voices pleaded. As soon as I succeeded in getting one bunch of bananas out of my face, three
more were shoved under my nose.

To get rid of the vendors, Huddy bought six bunches of
bananas. They quickly backed away, and then came back with
tomatoes and avocados. Before I could wipe the tomato juice

out of my eyes, and the avocado pulp from under my nose, a vendor came at me with a squawking chicken. The fowl flapped his wings in my face and deposited his droppings on my arm. In order to go scot free, we bought all the produce that was shoved in our faces. We piled it in the back seat of "Adam" and walked over to the precipice.

It is a magnificent view. The waters of Taal Lake extend for miles and miles and lap against the shores of distant purple-tinged mountains. Little bancas, or canoes, with red and yellow sails skim across the lake like colored water bugs. In the center of the lake is Taal Volcano, which rises up like an inverted bowl with the bottom squared off, and on top of the crater is another lake. It is difficult to believe this peaceful volcano was once a demon that belched flames and spat cinders. In an eruption over fifteen years ago, it completely destroyed the city of Tagaytay Ridge and killed 2,300 people.

Below us was a fertile valley laid out in squares of green and yellow which reminded me of a great patchwork quilt. The nipa huts resembled little match boxes and the women working in the rice paddies were little folk in a fairy book.

When we returned to "Adam," we found all of the produce we had piled in the back seat had been stolen. The vendors were now busy shoving bananas in the faces of the newcomers who had just driven up. We quickly drove away before we had to rebuy our produce.

We ate lunch at the picnic grounds, a large coconut grove that overlooks Taal Lake. This had always been a popular spot with Army and Navy personnel, as well as with Manila residents. The vendors at the picnic ground were less aggressive and sold a better type of garden products. Near the entrance of the picnic ground is a crude sign which reads: "Horuses to rent" (sic), and the soldiers were having a field day riding the dwarfish ponies with their feet dragging the ground.

As we started back to Manila, I was a bit uneasy. We had

been warned not to be out after dark, for the bandits might take our jeep from us and leave us tied up to a coconut tree. It was a long way back to town, and I had no desire to enter the city via bull cart.

I might have been less apprehensive about "Adam" had not our good friends, the Forest Bartls, had their jeep stolen just the week before despite the fact that Forest had bought a heavy logging chain which he locked around the steering wheel and for extra precaution locked another heavy chain around a front wheel, drawing the chain through the window and attaching it to the head of his bed. No one could possibly steal the jeep without rousing him! The Bartls slept peacefully. The next morning all was well, for the chain was still locked to the bedpost . . . but the jeep was gone. A clever thief had quietly sawed the chains. The Bartls never saw their jeep again.

It was reported that two hundred Army jeeps were stolen each day in Manila. They were driven to a well-concealed shop on the outskirts of the city and converted into jeepneys. This conversion crew worked with such speed that should your jeep be stolen one night, the very next afternoon you might step into a bright-red jeepney and pay twenty centavos fare, and like as not it would be your own conveyance of the day before.

We had been lucky, for "Adam" was still our jeep and not a jeepney. For this we thanked our good friend and neighbor, Mr. Noel, who had suggested we keep our jeep inside his high-fenced yard. It was quite a ritual each night to bed down "Adam." He was assigned to the far corner of the yard, alongside several other jeeps. After he was backed into position, we locked the steering wheel with a heavy padlock, then placed tin cans filled with rocks on the top; other rattling cans were set on the fenders; then we attached rattling objects underneath. Should the thieves remove the tin cans, the concealed rattlers would rouse the dogs.

We had to be constantly on the lookout. One day, my good

friend, Alise Jones, who lived across the street, was taking a siesta upstairs. Her houseboy slipped cat-like into the room and pitched her clothes out of the window. His buddy was standing underneath the window to catch them. The two boys made their getaway in the Jones' jeep.

Alise would trust no one. "They'll steal the roof from over your head—that is, if you don't sleep on it."

The jeep stealing was a fact; the roof stealing a fantasy. Or so I had believed. However, on this day, while we were hurrying down Tagaytay Road with "Adam" doing his very best, around forty miles per hour, we sighted a strange-looking object moving slowly down the middle of the road.

"Looks like a house," I remarked, glimpsing the size and the shape of it.

"It couldn't be a house," Huddy replied. "The thing has legs." And so it did. About a dozen brown legs were moving along. "Why it must be a mammoth thousand leg." I blurted out, still confused.

"Who ever heard of a thousand leg wearing BVD's?" said my smart husband. And just as he spoke, I, too, had observed that each brown leg was clad in khaki-colored underwear, regular GI issue. Before I could make another guess we had come upon the object. It was a thatched roof being whisked down the road by a dozen Filipinos. The only visible portion of them was their legs poking underneath the roof.

"Oh heavens!" I gasped. "They have stolen someone's roof." Right away I bade Huddy to stop the jeep so I might take a picture of the scene. I would run the picture and the story on the front page of the Manila *Times*. I'd show 'em!

Huddy argued I had better keep my nose from under this roof before someone whacked it off with a bolo knife. I paid him no mind but ran down the road with my camera. Just as I reached the project, a man, no doubt the chief of this roof-stealing gang, poked his head out to look at me. I drew back quickly lest I should be de-nosed just like Huddy had said. The man greeted me with a big smile. "Ah," he said, "this is going to be a big surprise." And he indicated the roof. And, thinks I, indeed it will be a surprise when someone rouses from his siesta to find the hot sun pouring down on his head.

"You know Juan de la Cruz?" asked the chief as he walked along beside me, for by this time I was under the roof keeping step with the gang of thieves. I could hear Huddy calling to me to get back to the jeep, but I was determined to find out a few things.

"Right this minute, Juan is at church and he doesn't know what goes on," said the chief to me, in great confidence. By this time I was beginning to feel like one of the gang.

Now, to steal a roof from over someone's head when one siestas is not right; but to steal a roof when one kneels to pray is unforgivable. Had this gang of thieves attended the little church across the rice field as poor Juan had, this would not have happened. But who was I to preach? I had not gone to church; neither had I stolen a roof.

The dozen Filipinos, wearied of their burden, set it down to rest themselves. They gathered around me to talk. Old men, young men, and little boys, all talking about this roof-moving as if it were a good neighbor act. It struck me they all had such honest faces and such generous smiles. In fact, they were the nicest gang of thieves I ever heard of. I liked them.

I learned their story. Juan de la Cruz was a very old man who lost his right leg during a Jap bombing; he had also lost his family and his home. This thatched roof had lain in the far corner of the rice field for goodness knows how long. The good neighbors got together and planned to move the roof over to Juan's little piece of land while he was at church. It was to be a big surprise. By and by they would get together and build Juan a nice nipa hut. Even the little boys were entering into this good neighbor spirit.

I had heard my grandmother speak of such things. Good neighbors would gather to husk corn, to plow a field, or to hew logs to build a house for a less fortunate neighbor. Such folk were the salt of the earth; such hospitality was the foundation upon which America was built. Now here I found the same spirit in the Philippines.

Chapter Six

◈﷽ I CONTEND that any American woman who experienced grocery shopping in an Army Commissary in the Philippines after liberation could easily qualify for a job in the Marine Corps and slug it out on the toughest beachhead.

We were rationed on food at the Commissary. Our family of three was allowed forty dollars worth of groceries per week. Only one member of the family could hold the card and enter the Commissary due to the crowded conditions. This was my assignment each Wednesday. Even Josie was not permitted to accompany me. Tony, the U.S. government driver of the jeep, could step inside the Commissary door and carry out my heavy basket.

I always dreaded to face the ration clerks. It appeared they knew my grocery needs better than I did, and they had control over our purchases. They would carefully check my list, then snitch away four cans of fruit I needed and replace these with four cans of Drano that I had no use for.

In the early days, I simply couldn't bring myself to shove and push. I would step aside very politely while the other women cleaned the shelves of groceries. They would grab, snatch, even pull hair for that last can of coffee on the shelf. Had I known what to expect in making this commissary run, I would have taken a course in jujitsu before I left the States. However, I was soon broken in. I learned to gore a woman with my elbow and clean the shelves of scarce items quicker than most of the shoppers.

I remember once the check clerk scratched out four cans of soup on my list and asked me why on earth I didn't get a bar of soap instead. A bar of soap! That was indeed a prize! I must have resembled old "Man o' War" as I raced down the length of that commissary neck and neck with a tough old army sergeant who had also been informed by the ration clerk that he was entitled to this precious item. He had the advantage; he had served in the South Pacific theatre of war, so he beat me by a nose and grabbed the last bar of soap. I returned to my basket, which I had left in the middle of the floor, to find someone had helped themselves to a can of coffee and two pounds of bacon.

On the day the Thanksgiving turkeys arrived from the States, I was permitted to recruit two Filipino boys from my husband's office to accompany me. On this day I was run down by a battalion of army wives charging with the fury of an All-American football team toward the turkeys.

These brave lads came to my rescue. That is, they rushed up to me, shoved a woman's foot out of my face, and groomed me for the next charge. This time I made it only to find the last turkey on the counter was a big plump bird with the right leg whacked off. That often happened, for the boys back in the warehouse would chop off a leg, wrap it up, and carry it home to eat with rice. Nevertheless, this amputated object was a turkey and Thanksgiving was at hand.

With the constant danger of being out after dark, in these post-war days, a high-jacker might steal the jeep, the groceries, or even me. Tony, aware of such danger, was always in such a hurry that he would start the jeep before I got my other foot in.

The streets of Manila were full of shell holes, so big that in rainy weather the carabaos could wallow in them. Tony knew every hole; he would take a running start and the jeep would do a broad jump to clear the hole. Now don't ask me how. On this occasion I was clutching my one-legged turkey for dear life when Tony started this jeep maneuver. I closed my eyes for I had a feeling I would soon be astride the old water buffalo bathing in the shell hole.

This time we didn't make it. The apples, the turkey, and I scattered in different directions. Before I could get upright, a group of boys, apparently waiting for the spill, made off with my turkey.

The next morning the doctor grabbed his cap. After all, this was Thanksgiving and we were far from home. His family would have a Thanksgiving turkey! He had a beaming grin on his face when he returned an hour later. He had gone to a little black market stall down on Echague Street, and bought an American turkey for fifty pesos. Twenty-five American dollars.

Harvel and I grabbed the prize package from under his arm and eagerly tore into it. Gad! A big plump turkey with its right leg chopped off!

Food was our biggest problem. We were forbidden to eat the fresh vegetables trucked down from Baguio and sold in the local markets, unless they were boiled, for fear we would get amoebic dysentery. The truck gardening was done in such a haphazard way—human refuse was used as fertilizer and open sewers turned on the land to irrigate.

Even the vegetables shipped in from the States and sold at the commissary were not to be eaten raw, unless they were soaked in Microklen, a disinfectant distributed by the Army. The handlers in the commissaries were often carriers of the dreaded amoeba. By the time crisp lettuce had a Microklen bath, it wasn't fit to eat. We didn't buy small native eggs, either, because we did not know how the chickens were cared for. Besides, they were thirty cents a piece.

I liked to go to the market with Josie. Of course American women never went to market, nor did upper-class Filipina women. But I loved it. Josie taught me the names of the native vegetables and fruits. I never permitted Josie to walk six paces behind me; she walked proudly by my side in her stiff white uniform, her dark hair piled high with a white gardenia tucked behind her ear. She was a pretty girl. At first, I was quite a novelty to the Philippine residents. They crowded about to see Josie's "Mom."

I always wore tennis shoes when I went to Quiapo Market, for it was damp, and in the fish stalls the water was always running ankle deep. There must have been four hundred stalls in the fish market. And there was a Filipino behind each, constantly pouring fresh water over the fish to keep them fresh.

The fish stalls, although sloppy and messy, fascinated me. There were huge fish, small fish, smelly dried fish, prawns, oysters, and eel. The minute we appeared, the vendors would rush up and stick a big flopping fish under my nose. "Buy him, Mom." Josie would get the vendors out of the way and we would go on. Soon another would shove a fish, no longer floundering, at me. "Very fresh fish, Mom."

"Don't truth her, Mom," Josie would say. That was her way of meaning don't believe her. I liked to hear the songs of the fish wives. It was a chant that rang out the length of the market. They would stand, feet wide apart, and with both hands hoist a big fish high overhead. They would sway their bodies rhythmically and sing a little ditty in Tagalog, that went: "Buy my fish! Buy my fish today."

We would go to the vegetable markets and Josie would teach me the names of native vegetables. Fresh tomatoes, bombay beans, umphalia, opo, sweet melons, and greens of every kind. Any kind of a green, cooked or raw, is called salad. An aged woman slept with her head resting on piles of spinach, if you wanted to buy her produce you had to shake her vigorously; others sat over small charcoal stoves cooking rice for the noonday meal; two women would sit beside a stall and one would be picking lice out of the other's head.

Josie would always search out a clean portion of the market for vegetables and fish. Then she would bargain. She never paid the asking price for any item. If it were one peso, she would say: "I give you fifty centavos," and usually she settled for sixty centavos. I grew so accustomed to bargaining that Huddy was sure I would disgrace him when we returned to the States. "Likely," he said, "you will walk into Neiman Marcus in Dallas and when they show you a dress for one hundred dollars, you'll blurt out: 'I'll give you fifty.'"

Outside Quiapo Market we always met the orchid vendor. The bamboo yoke across his shoulders was covered with beautiful flowering tree orchids and leis of sweet sampaguita. I usually went home wearing several leis and with arms loaded with tree orchids.

We often had to do without meat from one commissary day to the next. I dared not buy enough to last, because of "Old Diablo's" fits of temperament which would cause spoilage. The Cold Stores in Manila always had carabao meat and tough meat from Australia which we could not eat.

We had been hungry for good American meat. Huddy came home and said he had sighted a red and black funnel on a ship. That meant an American President Liner had docked. We knew it brought over a shipment of meat. He suggested I go very early to Luzon Market and get a beef roast, steaks, chops, and frozen liver. This amount of meat would cost fifty pesos. I put the money he gave me in my purse, grabbed a taxi, and hurried off, so I could get my pick of the good cuts.

Just as I was about to enter the store, a group of Moro pearl vendors swarmed around me, shoving pearls in my face, begging me to buy. I was very careful to clutch my purse tightly in my right hand, while I "shoo-d" the vendors away with my left. One lone vendor lingered. He crept closer and closer, then took from his pocket a tiny piece of folded paper and slowly unwrapped it. He dangled before my eyes an enormous black pearl. "Mom" he whispered confidentially, "for you this magic black pearl only one hundred pesos."

"No." I said quickly, remembering the family was hungry for good American meat. But he was fully aware the beauty of the jewel had captivated me. "Just for you, my American friend. Just for you. Eighty pesos. For anyone else it would be one hundred and fifty pesos."

It amused me that he should make such a concession in the price, just for me, an American he had never seen before. I told him it was a lovely gem and tried to dismiss him. As I walked toward the entrance to the store, he walked backwards right in front of me, holding the black pearl temptingly up in front of my eyes, turning it so the sunlight would pick up countless colored stars that seemed to dance on its satin lustre.

"How much you pay?" He had started again. I did not bargain for I had with me only the money for the meat. "You pay me seventy-five pesos; it is yours. Just for you." I tried to enter the store with the pearl vendor riding on my toes. With each step he had reduced the price of this magnificent pearl. In a fit of exasperation I yelled, "No! No!" He left me and was soon riding on the toes of another American woman who was entering the store.

Just as I had banished the pearl vendor, here came another with a star sapphire. I brushed him aside, but another vendor promptly took his place. He held before my eyes an alexandrite, a magnificent gem. "Mom, just for you, fifty pesos." I still resisted. "Please Mom, just for you. It is the only one of its kind in the Islands. It belonged to my mother. But for you only fifty pesos." The stone about the size of a grain of corn lay in the palm of his hand. It turned yellow, purple, and a deep fiery red. Its beauty captivated me. "Mom, just for you. Fifty pesos." He moved his hands a bit and the colors of the stone changed like a chameleon. It fascinated me. I handed the Moro the fifty pesos.

He was gone. I glanced at the meat counter—beef, pork chops, lamb chops, calves' liver—every choice cut one could wish for. I watched the American women crowding toward the counter, filling their baskets.

I must hurry home, put on my tennis shoes, and go with Josie to the fish market.

I tried to explain to Huddy as we sat down to eat our fish and rice that we would finish a roast in one meal, but this beautiful alexandrite I would have for a lifetime. It was a precious gem, I explained, no other one like it in the Islands. It had belonged to the Moro's mother.

"How much did it cost?"

"Only fifty pesos."

He drew from his pocket an alexandrite that he had bought from a Moro. It, too, had belonged to the Moro's mother. It was a larger and more magnificent stone than the one I held in my hand.

"How much did it cost?" I asked.

"Ten pesos."

After we moved from the little white house to a quonset hut in the American Embassy Compound, I made up my mind to be less of a problem child—after all, my husband was doing a big and a difficult job here in the Philippines. And I was sure that often I was his biggest problem. Every time he came home he cast that *"now* what have you been up to" look at me.

The Fourth of July was at hand. To be sure, the American Flag would wave from the Embassy Building and over the Army installations, but I wanted a flag of my own this Fourth of July. Back in the States I had taken my flag for granted. Sure, sometimes my neighbor would raise a flag; maybe I would, maybe I wouldn't. I could run down to the corner drug store and buy one. But to be in a foreign country unable to buy your own flag—well, it gives one a desolate feeling.

The Japanese had burned every American flag they could lay hands on, and there had not been time for the stores to get in a new shipment. Besides, this was the first Independence Day of the new Republic of the Philippines and they were interested in selling their own brand-new flag, the Sun and Stars.

Huddy and I were walking down Dasmariñas Street, when we came upon a little stand selling fireworks and flags. I spied a lone American flag stuck in a bamboo bucket alongside the Sun and Stars. I rushed up and grabbed it. Huddy simply put his foot down; I should not pay twenty pesos (ten American dollars) for such a little flag. "Why, you could buy this small flag for ten cents in any Woolworth store back home," he said. Reluctantly I replaced it in the bamboo bucket.

We strolled leisurely down Dasmariñas, then crossed over to the Escolta. I kept looking at my watch. "Shouldn't you be getting back to your office?" I asked. He seemed in no hurry; so we ambled leisurely along. Finally he told me goodby and headed for the Heacock Building. As soon as he was out of sight, I made tracks back to the little stand, hoping that no other American had discovered the little flag. I was so overjoyed to find it still there, that I thrust a twenty peso bill into the boy's hand and didn't even try to bargain.

As I turned to leave, the boy asked: "Say, do you know Harvard?"

"Harvard?"

"Yes, Harvard. Do you know Harvard back in the States?"

"Do you mean Harvard University?"

"Yes, that's the Harvard I mean."

Then he bragged that he was the houseboy for a man who had graduated from Harvard. "I go there sometime, maybe," he said.

That night we were to attend a pre-Fourth dinner at the Army and Navy Club and the plates were twenty pesos each. When Huddy came back from his office, I announced that I was going to stay home. (I would be a martyr and starve because he had forbidden me to buy the little flag.) When he pinned me down for a good reason, I simply waved the flag in his face. Of course it ended up with the flag going with me to the Army and Navy Club.

The little flag was the toast of the evening. Never have I seen a group of Americans so enjoy this emblem. They took turns at waving it; the women kissed the red and white stripes; we all joined in singing "The Star Spangled Banner." The little flag brought us very close together, very close that night to our own America the Beautiful across the Pacific.

The next day, the Fourth of July, the little flag was a high-flying one over the door of our quonset hut in the American Embassy Compound. Out of the thirty quonsets, it was the only one with a flag. The neighbors gathered to admire it. And where on earth did I find it? By this time Huddy was bragging "Why, she paid ten American dollars for that flag! Yes sir, she did!"

Chapter Seven

∽ OUR NEW LIVING QUARTERS in the American Embassy Compound were located on Dewey Boulevard (now called Roxas Boulevard). The Embassy Building, once the palatial residence of Paul McNutt, High Commissioner, was in shambles but was being rebuilt. The large area surrounding it had been filled in by pumping sand from Manila Bay, and on this land were erected thirty quonset huts, salvaged from the army, to be used as living quarters for U.S. Government personnel.

We were privileged to live in the Embassy Compound because it was necessary to have a medical officer living on the premises. Our little quonset by the sea commanded a magnificent view, but it was so close to the bay that great foamy sprays swept over the top of it and sometimes filled our coffee cups and drenched our toast. We often wished for a patio umbrella to stretch over the breakfast bar. During the years we lived beside Manila Bay, I can't recall a time when we slept in a dry bed. When the monsoon winds howled, a very fine mist penetrated everything. We could crawl between soggy sheets, burrow down in a little hole, and let the warmth of our bodies dry out the spot. We dared not turn over. We would spread a raincoat over our heads and pillows to keep dry.

Fortunately our clothes were kept dry in a hot closet. This airtight closet was wired for electricity and several 100-watt bulbs burned all the time. Otherwise, a four-inch beard would sprout

overnight on the toes of our shoes, and our dresses would be too
limp to wear.

We felt secure in the Embassy Compound. No longer need
we live behind iron-barred windows, or duck the path of machine-gun bullets at night. The compound was under army
guard; no one entered the gates without a pass. A guard walked
the sea wall around the clock. This was necessary, for thieves
could paddle up to the wall in a small banca, leap over, rob a
quonset, and silently slip away with the loot.

Yet I missed the little white house in Pasay. I missed Harvel's
little school under the mango tree, a colorful drama that I was
not to have in the dignified Embassy Compound. I missed
Belén, squatted over the little Filipino washtub. I remembered
the first casualty: my dainty, lace-trimmed batiste blouse that
was too fragile to survive the whacks of her paddle. I also remembered that the seat of Huddy's white linen trousers were
also incapacitated. Belén could not do the laundry without her
paddle. She had not moved with us to the government quarters.
We hired Benita, a lavandera who did beautiful work. We had
built-in tubs in the laundry room underneath the quonset. I
bought a washboard at the Army PX to lighten the laundry work.
One morning I looked out and saw Benita arriving, lugging her
Filipino washtub. Later when I went downstairs, I found her
sitting on the washboard, as she squatted over the little tub,
washing clothes by hand, as she had done her whole lifetime.
How could I interfere?

My little quonset by the sea was one of the most attractive
apartments I shall ever have. It was built on stilts to keep the
flood waters from coming in. Underneath was a car port, a sun
porch filled with orchids, servants' quarters with bath, and a
small studio for my writing.

Huddy had spent a lot of money getting the studio ready for
me, and he was very proud of it. But I could not work in it. I

would slip down cautiously and peep in to see if a big python was snoozing on my desk. This fear was prompted by a news story in the Manila *Times* . . . a big thirteen-foot python was found sleeping under a front porch just six blocks away. And when roused from his nap, he had tried to swallow a small boy. I feared this thirteen-footer might have a mate lurking in our vicinity, and some bright morning when I was concentrating on Chapter Seven, he would slither into my studio and swallow me with one gulp. I fancied Huddy coming home, going down to the studio and finding only my shoes and my typewriter. To have piece of mind, I moved my desk upstairs.

The quonset had a charm all its own. There was a very large living room furnished with rattan furniture, deep lounging chairs, tea carts, lamps, tables with chinese red tops, and book cases. The kitchen was built like a little bar right in the center of the room, and we sat on bar stools to eat our breakfast while looking out over the bay. Ferns and orchids completely hid . . . guess who? . . . yes, "Old Diablo," who would not be with us much longer. His shiny new electric replacement was due any day. There were doors that led to the bedrooms. These I painted Chinese red and decorated with Chinese symbols meaning "Home Sweet Home," which were written down for me by a Chinese friend. It was a gay and a happy little home.

Each morning, from my bedroom, I greeted ships from many lands, that had docked during the night. These ships and I became such good friends that I named them as I would pets "Good morning, Red Lady," I greeted a ship from Holland, painted white with a wide red band around its middle. "Texas Girl" was a Lykes Brothers' freighter; and "Mimi" was from France. I always scanned the bay for a tall red and black funnel that soared high over the stacks of other ships. The American President Lines! This ship usually brought new personnel arriving to join the American Colony; or, good fresh meat from the States.

From my bedroom I looked out on the graveyard of sunken battleships, many with hulks half-submerged; others with noses buried in the water. Hundreds of ships had gone down and left only their rusty stacks poking up through the water. These resembled a great burned-out forest with the charred tree trunks remaining.

It was at this time that Julie came to us. She was Josie's younger sister, and the two girls had been separated for eight years. She had come to visit Josie, and if she could find work, she would like to remain and go to school. She had not been able to attend school since the war.

Josie came to me. "Mom, if we can keep Julie so she can go to school, she wants no pay. I'll teach her how to work your way, Mom. She can work in the afternoons." We kept Julie, but we paid her a fair wage. She enrolled in the Mission School which was within walking distance of the compound.

Julie, a sweet innocent girl right out of the province, became our pride and joy. She took her first shower with her clothes on. She was afraid of the electric current, and wouldn't open the new General Electric refrigerator. She shied away from the electric iron, and when she gained enough courage to use it, she would not disconnect it. If Josie were not around, she would run to me, "Mom, come quick and kill the iron."

One day she came up from the laundry room to the kitchen to heat a kettle of water to make starch. While she was waiting for the water to boil, several friends dropped in. She hesitated about walking in front of the guests with the pan of water, so she asked my permission in a loud voice. "Mom, may I pass my water in the living-room?"

The Embassy Compound grounds were planted in grass, and there were many banana and papaya trees, but even so the grounds seemed bleak. Josie and I decided to plant a flower bed around our quonset. The sandy soil was so impoverished, flowers would not thrive. So we drove "Adam" up Tagaytay Road and gathered rich loam in a coconut grove. We made many such trips and filled a large flower bed, six feet wide, that ran the length of the quonset and across the front of it. On the sea wall side, flowers did not thrive because of the salty spray.

We had no garden implements, so we borrowed a shovel from the tool shop at the Embassy. This shovel and a butcher knife were our means of tilling the soil. We had to dig very carefully for fear we would excavate a demolition bomb and be blown to bits. A workman finishing up the front steps of one of the quonsets had unearthed one. Many times we heard explosions, over on Dewey Boulevard, and the next day the newspaper would report that small boys were killed by bombs when they were poking about in the ruins of buildings. So with extreme caution and a butcher knife, we planted the first garden in the American Embassy grounds.

A cadena de amor climbed over our latticed sun porch, and tall Spanish canna lilies grew high as our heads. Josie planted a squash vine that grew so high it reached the top of the quonset. The six-inch leaves gave complete protection from rain and sun. We paid four dollars for a package of zinnia seed, but the blossoms were as large as saucers. We were the envy of every person living in the compound. Even Ambassador O'Neal came down to compliment us on our garden.

There was an agricultural station near Pasay that furnished free plants, trees, shrubs, and fertilizer. One day when we were there, I noticed a big bin of manure in a far corner. I decided we should get several baskets to fertilize our garden. I asked Josie to speak to the man in charge of the manure, for he could only speak Tagalog. Josie was very embarrassed. "Oh, Mom," she said, "I can't ask the man for the shit of the cow." I suggested she ask for manure or droppings. She would not compromise.

As we gathered up our baskets and headed for the bins, Josie lagged behind. I walked right up to the pile of manure, and with sign language made known I wanted three baskets. So I bargained without further embarrassment to Josie.

In the far corner of the Embassy Compound, within a stone's throw of our beautiful flower garden, stood a large quonset hut, and across the front was written: "WAR CRIMES TRIALS." It was a barren ugly spot. Even the cadena de amor that grew around the door languished and died. Too many footsteps had trampled it.

In front of the hut were parked Army staff cars, jeeps, and army trucks. The big brass, carrying bulging briefcases, hurried inside; Japanese lawyers with "dead pan" faces followed them. For here, on trial for their lives, were the Japanese who had so ruthlessly murdered, in cold blood, many Philippine civilians.

Other trials were under way near the old Normal School. The Philippine Government, in keeping with its sovereignty, in March, 1947, took over the prosecution of the Japanese accused of war crimes committed against the Philippine people. The first War Crimes Commission to be formed under Executive Order No. 68, was the one which tried and condemned the notorious "Butcher of the Bay," Captain Chusiro Kudo. Its members were Majors Salvador Rivero, Rigoberto Atienza, Mamerto Montelayor (president), and Carmelo Barbeyro. This court tried around one hundred Japanese at a cost of around 700,000 pesos.

The first one convicted was Sergeant Yoshiaki Kodama, found guilty of mistreatment and torture of non-combatants in Solano, Nueva Vizcaya, during The Occupation. It was a disappointment to many when he got off with only twelve years at hard labor. Another trial that I sat through was that of Captain Takefumi Fujita. It was he who was responsible for the "zona" of around four hundred residents of Mandaluyong in November 1944. He should have drawn death, but was saved by a technicality and drew ninety-nine years in Sugamo Prison.

The most sensational trial was that of "The Butcher of the Bay." He alone was responsible for the murder of 23 people in Laguna in February, 1945, and tortured over one hundred others. The courtroom was filled with Filipinos who had suffered at his hands. Little boys and girls sat through the trial and wept silently; they were remembering the dying screams of their murdered parents. In the group was an aged man with his right leg cut off. He had been held down while it was hacked off; then the bloody leg had been smeared in his face, for no reason except to satisfy Kudo. These injured Filipinos sat stoically, praying in their hearts that justice would be meted out to this beast. As I listened to these atrocities I, too, prayed that he would be hanged, and that they'd let the old man who had lost his leg, spring the trap.

Kudo's trial was long and wearisome. He stalled for time to save his neck. He even brought witnesses from Japan; why, I do not know. But this I did understand—the military tribunal was not for revenge. It wanted only to mete out justice. So the "Butcher" was given every chance. However, the long wait irritated the injured Filipinos. One day as an MP led the prisoner from the room, we noticed that he carried a GI mess kit. Suddenly a woman whose face bore a scar of his torture, came up out of her seat and screamed: "Why, they even feed the son-of-a-bitch!"

When judgement day for Kudo arrived, we all sat tense. When the sentence—"you shall hang by the neck until you are dead"—was read, there came rousing cheers as if Kudo had just made a touchdown.

The "Butcher" was to die at Muntinglupa Prison. They erected a brand-new scaffold with thirteen steps and made a long noose out of good manila hemp. For on this scaffold, no doubt, many a Jap would be sentenced to die.

Time dragged on and on. Kudo grew fat in the death cell, while the children he had orphaned grew hungrier. At long last the day came. We gathered in the prison yard to watch the execution. I watched the prisoner mount the steps. I counted off six of them . . . then I went chicken-hearted . . . I even felt sorry for him. I, who had clapped my hands the loudest when the sentence was read. But remember I was only a woman! I saw only the bent figure of a man trying desperately to climb thirteen steps toward his doom.

I covered my eyes with my hands, but even so I could hear that thud-thud-thud of the remaining steps. I could hear the mumbled prayers of the chaplain. I heard the spring of the trap . . . then that awful silence. "The Butcher of the Bay" was finished. But those he had maimed would continue to hobble through life; the children he had orphaned would continue to cry themselves to sleep.

Chapter Eight

CORREGIDOR, THE ROCK, was just across Manila Bay. I have seen it in various moods . . . dark and gloomy like a great sleeping monster . . . I have seen its rugged peaks tangled with fluffy white clouds like a bridal veil . . . I have seen it turn blood red at sunset, as if it, too, were remembering. I was to live intimately with The Rock for several years, for my bedroom window framed it like a picture in a beautiful sea-scape. I felt very possessive about it, as if it belonged to me personally.

I shall always remember my first trip to Corregidor. Huddy, Harvel, and I crossed the Bay on a little army boat, the *Allombra*. We made our way among the vast sea of sunken battleships to reach this tadpole-shaped island, with its bulbous head pointed west to the China Sea, its tail curved toward Manila.

Manila had fallen on January 2nd, 1942, and all communication between Manila and Corregidor was cut off. General MacArthur had announced he must get a message through to Manila. But how? It was the gallant Philippine soldiers who came forward and offered to carry the General's message from Corregidor. These soldiers knew the Bay, and they knew how to handle a banca. They slipped away under cover of darkness, making no more noise than a small fish cutting through the water. The soldiers arrived in Cavite on the mainland, hid themselves under a load of straw on a bull cart and jogged into Manila past the Japanese sentries. They delivered the message.

89

I recalled General MacArthur's last hours on Corregidor. When conditions worsened, General Marshall, our Chief of the Army General Staff, suggested that Jean MacArthur and her young son, Arthur, be evacuated from Corregidor by submarine. President of the Philippines, Manuel Quezon and his wife, and High Commissioner and Mrs. Sayre were to leave Febuary 20th, by submarine, for Australia. Jean MacArthur refused to go. She and her son would remain beside her husband and share the fate of the garrison. Even as she gave her answer, she could hear the voice of "Tokyo Rose" coming over the radio, announcing that General MacArthur would be captured and brought to Japan and publicly hanged on the Imperial Plaza in Tokyo.

Very shortly, President Roosevelt ordered General MacArthur to Australia. General Jonathan A. Wainwright was left in command at Corregidor. So, on March 11th, 1942, at seven fifteen in the evening, General MacArthur, his wife, his son, and their Cantonese nurse, Ah Cheu, slipped down to South Dock and boarded PT-41. There was a flotilla of four battle-scarred PT boats to carry the General, his family, and seventeen servicemen.

As I stood remembering all this, I also recalled a cocktail party at the MacArthurs which Huddy and I had attended while on a recent quick trip to Tokyo. A group of army personnel were invited to the Embassy House where General and Mrs. MacArthur lived. The general stood tall and handsome in dress uniform, every inch a soldier, and yet every inch a showman, until Jean MacArthur appeared, tall and beautiful, dressed in black. The General, no longer a soldier, went forward to meet her, just a husband now, who adored her.

It was a delightful party. I recall one of the men glanced toward the piano and jokingly asked if this was the instrument he had taken along on the PT-41 to sneak off Corregidor to Australia. We all remembered the ugly rumors that General MacArthur had left behind seriously ill Army Nurses so he could take his furniture, including a piano, when he escaped Corregidor.

Such remarks always infuriated him, and he replied, "As all of you know, when we left Corregidor we carried one suitcase for each member of the family. Our chances that night as we shoved off were one to five that we'd even make it."

As Huddy, Harvel, and I walked toward Big Malinta Tunnel, history walked beside us—I remembered the surrender. General Wainwright made the difficult decision at 10:00 A.M. He sent for Major General Moore and Brigadier General Lewis C. Beebe, and told them:

"We can't hold out much longer. Maybe we could last through this day, but the end certainly must come tonight. It would be better to clear up the situation now, in daylight."

So it was that at 10.00 A.M. on May 6, 1942, the order was issued from General Wainright's headquarters in the tunnel telling all units to prepare for surrender. The troops were ordered to destroy all weapons greater than .45 caliber before noon, along with equipment, supplies, transportation, and the few ships or boats still afloat.

At 10:30 A.M. General Beebe spoke into the microphone of "The Voice of Freedom":

"Message for General Homma . . . Message for General Homma, or the present commander in chief of the Imperial Japanese Forces on Luzon.

"Anyone receiving this message please transmit it to the commander in chief of the Imperial Japanese Forces on Luzon.

"For military reasons which General Wainwright considers sufficient, and to put a stop to further sacrifice of human life, the Commanding General will surrender to Your Excellency today the four fortified islands at the entrance to Manila Bay together with all military and naval personnel and all existing stores and equipment . . ."

Between repetitions of the surrender broadcast, General Wainwright radioed his last messages to General MacArthur and to the President of the United States, saying good-bye and summing up the reasons for his action.

The white flag of surrender slowly went up the Topside flagpole promptly at noon, as Colonel Paul D. Bunker carried out the orders from General Wainwright.

Refusing to recognize this international symbol of truce, the Japs continued their attack from the air, the sea, and the ground. So, half an hour later General Beebe for the fourth time repeated the radio message. But it was not for another thirty minutes that enemy fire slackened

With General Moore and their personal aides, General Wainwright left the tunnel and rode to the enemy lines. "Playful" enemy machine gunners on Denver Hill sprayed rounds on both sides of the car and a fleet of Japanese planes dropped bombs not far away. As the officers got out of the car, to walk up Denver Hill, two more fleets of Jap bombers attacked Port Hughes, which also had been flying the white flag for nearly two hours.

A Jap lieutenant stood in the middle of the road silently, scornfully surveying the surrender party, and a Jap private came forward and snatched a pair of field glasses that hung around the neck of Colonel John R. Pugh, one of General Wainwright's aides. The officer, named Uemura, was able to speak English. "We will not accept your surrender," he snarled, "unless it includes all American and Filipino troops in the whole archipelago."

"I do not choose to discuss surrender terms with you," General Wainwright told him, and requested to be taken to the senior Jap officer on Corregidor. There suddenly appeared a Jap colonel. He could speak no English and Lieutenant Uemura acted as interpreter.

General Wainwright told the colonel he was offering the surrender of the four forts—Mills, Hughes, Drum, and Frank.

The Jap colonel insisted that General Wainwright must surrender all of the Philippine Forces.

General Wainwright demanded that he be allowed to deal with General Homma, and the Jap colonel agreed that such a meeting could be arranged at Cabcaben, on Bataan.

The colonel took General Wainwright and his party back to Kindley Field, near the landing beach where the Jap barges were still bringing in reinforcements. There the Japs had set up a radio station and the colonel messaged for a boat from Cabcaben for the trip. When they arrived at Cabcaben, the Jap informed General Wainwright that he would be able to talk with General Homma at a house, about a quarter mile north, where General Homma had his headquarters. The surrender party drove there directly.

The official surrender document, already signed, was handed by General Wainwright to General Homma who turned it over to his interpreter, a Lieutenant Nakamura, and it was read aloud to the Jap general. He informed General Wainwright, through the interpreter, that no surrender would be accepted unless it included all of the United States and Filipino troops under General Wainwright's command.

When General Wainwright continued arguing his position, General Homma suddenly arose, announced that he would continue operations against Corregidor, and walked out on the conference.

General Wainwright and his staff were left sitting alone, except for the interpreter and the colonel who had brought them from Corregidor. General Wainwright asked what would be done at this time. The interpreter replied that they would be returned to Corregidor, where they could do as they "damn please."

The party was taken back, landed at North Point, and they waded ashore. General Beebe, who was quite ill, had to be carried. They made their way back to the east entrance of the tunnel.

During the surrender conference, despite the truce, the Japanese had pushed their lines forward to within one hundred yards of the east tunnel entrance. General Wainwright, maddened by this breach of military ethics, sharply ordered the interpreter to take him immediately to the Japanese commander.

The interpreter took General Wainwright and his party around Malinta Hill to the little Filipino civilian barrio near the shore of San José Bay where the Jap headquarters had been set up. General Wainwright there met Col. Denhichi Sato, commanding officer of the attacking forces, who stood in the market place. He informed General Wainwright that he was about to attack Topside with troops who had landed during the afternoon on San José Beach after the surrender flag had gone up.

Subject to annihilation on every side, General Wainwright announced he was ready to meet the full demands of General Homma. A new surrender document was typed by the Japs at their CP.

In the feeble candlelight, General Wainwright scribbled his signature. It was midnight, May 6, 1942.

Early in the morning, General Wainwright, under guard, was taken to the west entrance of the tunnel, passing by many of his men who had been rounded up that afternoon and the evening before and were now under guard. Many of them shook his hand or patted him on the shoulder as he passed.

At the time of Corregidor's fall, there were nearly 12,000 Americans and Filipinos in the island garrison. More than 1,500 of these were sick and wounded, in the hospital. Hundreds of others were shell shocked. Many of the ill had been brought from Bataan the night before its fall on April 9th. Gaunt from exhaustion and starvation, and feverish with malaria, they had spent the whole month in the thick, dust-clogged air of the tunnel, hoping vainly for deliverance.

Nearly eight hundred Americans had been killed in the last fifteen hours of fighting.

Corregidor was lost to the world. Not for three long years were free men to know what had happened after that tragic day of May 6, 1942.

The American soldiers were sent to Cabanatuan Prison, while the Filipino soldiers went on to Camp O'Donnell from Corregidor and Bataan.

General Wainwright was interned at Kwarenko, Formosa.

Huddy, Harvel, and I walked over to San José Beach, to the spot where the surrender had taken place. Now it was a little shrine, just a tiny piece of earth not eight feet in diameter enclosed by chains linked to four mortar shells, one set at each corner. A little path beautified with white shells and small stones from the beach trace the footsteps of General Wainwright as he walked with bowed head and tears streaming down his cheeks to the surrender spot.

From Bottomside we rode in a jeep to Middleside to view the ruined barracks of the enlisted men, the largest barracks in the world; the hospital with its crumbling walls and each bombed-out window resembling the empty socket of an eye. Bougainvillea grew luxuriantly with bright blossoms amid the ruins.

At topside the huge old acacia trees, mowed down by constant shelling, stood charred and twisted like grotesque figures. We paused beside the historic flagpole where the white flag of surrender had gone up, where the Stars and Stripes had been hauled down and burned, and the flag of the Rising Sun hoisted. We paused to read General MacArthur's words written on the plaque: "Hoist the colors to its peak and let no enemy ever haul them down." I lifted my eyes to the top of the pole. Old Glory was flying high!

Harvel and I climbed up into the tower of the old Spanish Lighthouse, an historic landmark. The name Corregidor means "corrector" in Spanish. In the early days, before 1795, the Castillians had established a dockyard and naval convalescent hospital on the island. Corregidor was used as an outpost for a semaphore signal system to warn Manila of the approach of hostile ships, particularly the Moro pirates. The lighthouse was established in 1836 with a beam range of thirty-three miles. Corregidor, for a time, served as a small penal colony. Here, too, was a station for ships to have their papers corrected . . . hence the name Corregidor.

As we looked out over the bay, it was so beautiful with hardly a ripple on the water. Had there really been a war? Yes. Another reminder loomed up in the bay . . . magnificent Fort Drum, that stationary concrete battleship whose turreted guns were the last silenced by the enemy. All during the siege, Fort Drum was cornered, alone and unafraid. It was the quintessence of defiance; it fired until five minutes before surrender.

The army guard escorted Huddy, Harvel, and me to the lonely spot where the dead were buried. The ground was overgrown with weeds and grass. Once it had been a spot of ragged, battered white crosses made of simple sticks . . . sometimes nothing more than tent pegs. This was the last resting place of American and Philippine soldiers who had died during the years of 1941 and 1942. The Japanese had stolen most of the identification discs for souvenirs. Familiar names: Texas . . . Prairie Grove . . . Three Forks . . . Princeton . . . Bataan . . . Philippine Islands . . . Virginia . . . Grand Saline . . . San Antonio . . . Fayetteville . . . boys from almost every State in the Union and Philippine boys from the archipelago's various islands, who had baptized this solitary Rock with their blood . . . these were the boys who waited and waited and waited for the help that did not come. Huddy was visibly moved, and spoke frankly. "The Japs did not penetrate the Rock . . . they penetrated our own short-sightedness . . . our unpreparedness. The Rock was impenetrable."

As we stood at the entrance of Big Malinta Tunnel, I strained my ears to hear the cries of a Philippine army nurse. A guard at the Tunnel had brought news to Manila that each night at midnight there walked a ghost of an army nurse, up and down the long concourse, crying. It was the God's truth, he said. On this day we heard no cries, yet the story still intrigued me.

There were many messages scribbled on the walls of Malinta Tunnel. Some were written with pencil, barely legible; others were scratched with stone. Most of the messages were addressed to a mother. Two of the messages I copied in my notebook still haunt me. One reads: "My God, they are here (meaning the Japs) Mother, we are trapped like gophers in this hell-hole." The other, more touching: "Mother, if I could just run into your arms tonight, like I used to do when I was hurt." It was signed "David."

We were back in Manila. It had been a memorable day. I picked up my notebook that night, and wrote: "Corregidor—of eternal memory." No more.

I made many trips to Corregidor, for I could cross the bay on a little army boat that sailed each morning at ten o'clock from the dock right near the American Embassy and returned at three in the afternoon. Often I went just for the ride. I liked to stand on deck and get a close-up view of the sunken battleships; I loved to ride the big army trucks to Topside to enjoy the magnificent view.

The story about the army nurse crying each night still haunted me. So I persuaded Huddy and a group of others to go over to Corregidor and spend the night. One dark night, we took up watch in the Tunnel, with the army guard who had told us the story as our guide. We carried cameras and flashlights. We were all very quiet. We were concerned, for the story touched us deeply.

Around midnight a breeze swept down from Topside and

whipped through the tunnel. There was a wailing sound, very much like the cries of a woman, yet we saw no ghost.

Suddenly the guard cried out! "There she is! Can't you see her?" He ran over to the apparition and placed his hand on its shoulder. He saw her, so he told us, as plain as day.

Later I was told the boy died in a mental hospital.

I was on Corregidor the day the Sun and Stars of the Republic of the Philippines replaced the Stars and Stripes. This "Exchange of Flags" took place at high noon on October 12, 1947. I had gone over on the Press Boat, the dredge *Barth*, with a group of newsmen and photographers from around the world who were on hand to record this historic event. I was to write many stories about the Philippines, but this would remain in my mind as the most important story I ever covered. I recall the pressmen were a jolly bunch, but I sat alone and was sad. I realized this little army boat, loaded with newsmen, was making its last run— we were returning Corregidor to the Philippine Government.

The "Exchange of Flags" took place at the exact spot where the Stars and Stripes had been hauled down and burned on May 6, 1942, and the flag of Japan hoisted. On this day, our flag was to be hauled down again, for the second time in half a century, but it was to be replaced by a friendly flag, the flag of the Philippines.

The ceremony was consummated in the presence of high officials of the United States Armed Services and the Philippine Republic. Minutes before Old Glory was to be lowered, it waved serenely as if to take a last look at the scene below.

The Marine Band struck up the tune: "It's a grand old flag, It's a high flying flag," and the soldiers loosened the halyard to lower our colors. About six feet from the top of the flagpole, Old Glory fluttered out in the breeze . . . a dramatic gesture, as if to wave a last farewell. I was so touched that I wept unashamedly. Beside me stood a Filipino, who said in a choked voice, "I grew up under that flag." As I looked about me, I saw strong men—

both Army colonels and GI's—wiping the tears from their eyes. But we soon dried our tears and joined this new Republic to give three cheers for a brand-new flag, the Sun and the Stars.

We had promised to return this historic shrine to the Philippine Republic. This simple ceremony on the island of Corregidor proclaimed to the world that we, the United States of America, considered a promise made was a promise kept. That was the code of Old Glory.

If I had questioned the relinquishing of this historic bit of land, all doubts were banished when I heard the voice of President Manuel Roxas. His words were spoken long before Korea, yet it seemed that day he was addressing the aggressors of the Korean conflict that was soon to follow. And as I recall today, his message delivered very near a quarter of a century before Viet Nam, might very well be a message to the aggressors of this war-torn country.

"We, the Philippines, will work for peace, an enduring peace, for a just peace for all peoples, for the victors and the vanquished alike. We will continue the struggle for liberty, not only for ourselves, but for all men.

"We will strive to free ourselves and others from want and fear, and to promote the welfare and the happiness of every man. We will support the peaceful efforts of all nations to be free and to allow them to set up the governments of their choice. We will cooperate with other nations in establishing a world order under which each nation will have an opportunity to pursue the happiness and the prosperity of its citizens. We will demand in the council of the nations, the recognition of the principle that world peace is indivisible and that the world cannot remain half slave and half free. Corregidor is the indestructible monument to which I pledge these noble principles."

I glanced at Old Glory, now folded and resting with the stars up, tenderly, on the outstretched arms of a young Philippine soldier, wearing the uniform of the United States Army. I realized that, in spirit, my country was not leaving this historic piece of land. True, it had returned the mountains of Bataan and Corregidor, the trees, the grasses of the fields, and the sands of the shores, to their native land. But my heart told me, in that moment, that Corregidor and Bataan did not belong to any one nation, not even to the historic Philippines.

Corregidor and Bataan belonged to the ages and to all men who believed in human liberty. For these names were now enshrined in the temple of hope for all mankind along with Runnymede, Valley Forge, and all places where the fires of freedom were lighted and kept burning.

I may have felt possessive about Corregidor, because my heart had been there during the long, dark days of the war. For on this battered island the boys of The Fighting 200th of Taos, the doctor's boys, made their last stand. And New Mexico, my adopted State, lost more soldiers on Corregidor and Bataan than any other State.

On January 6, 1941, I had stood on the little Plaza de Taos, New Mexico, and waved good-bye to the 200th Coast Artillery, off for training. I remember I ran down the road a ways and waved again and again as my heart called out . . . good-bye! good-bye! Little did I know that a few years later I was to join the doctor who was on duty in the Philippines, and that I would stand on the shores of historic old Manila Bay and wave good-bye to the *U.S.S. Lt. Boyce* as it bore our war dead home . . . that I would run down Pier No. 5 a little ways and wave again and again as my heart again called out . . . goodbye, goodbye! . . . for many of the bodies in the flag-draped caskets aboard the *Lt. Boyce* were those of the boys to which I had waved goodbye back in the little Taos Plaza.

Military Cemetery No. 2, near Manila, known as Balintawak, was the temporary resting place of our fallen boys, heroes of Bataan and Corregidor. It was a beautiful spot with fifteen thousand white crosses set in a field of green grass. In the distance, the Mariveles—the Death March Mountains—rose like sentinels, and their purple peaks tangled with clouds reminiscent of the Sangre de Cristo mountains of Taos.

During the winter months the glorious sunsets of the Orient settled over Balintawak and tinged the white crosses a rosy red; in springtime the huge old acacia trees that dotted the cemetery, burst into full bloom and the soft pink petals fell gently upon the graves.

Each Memorial Day, Huddy and I visited Military Cemetery No. 2. As we walked among the white crosses, I fancied our boys could hear our footsteps, feel our presence, hear our voices as we whispered each name when we paused beside each grave. We were seized with a feeling of loneliness when we learned the *Lt. Boyce* was to return these boys to their own United States. This ship was the first army transport to sail to the Orient to bring home our war dead.

It was a clear morning in Manila. Overhead it was as blue as a New Mexico sky. The *Lt. Boyce* with the caskets already carried on board, stood alongside Military Pier No. 5, waiting for final rites before weighing anchor. I shall never forget the beauty of this ship of the dead. A solid line of wreaths of roses were hanging from the railings, both starboard and port, and from prow to stern—even the riggings were twined with flowers. There was a hushed stillness. Even the blue waters of Manila Bay lashed the sides of the ship ever so gently, as if they, too, knew.

High officials of the Army, Navy, and the Philippine Republic, together with a solemn uncovered crowd, gathered at the pier for the ceremony. We stood with bowed heads as we listened to the chaplain's words: "Blessed be their memory . . ." a fitting sequel to General Moore's tribute: "Comrades in life. Comrades in death in the Sanctuary of the Dead." The quietness of the moment was broken by a canopy of planes from Clark Field

showering rose petals that fell on the deck of the *Lt. Boyce,*
on the caskets, over the crowd, and even on the pages of the
chaplain's prayer book. The rites were said, taps sounded, and
the *Lt. Boyce* weighed anchor.

A flotilla of small army boats escorted the funeral ship to
breakwater, scattering rose petals on the waves. Overhead,
an armada of planes dropped huge wreathes of roses, many falling on the deck of the ship, others settling on the waves. As the
Marine Detachment of the United States Naval Forces played
"Going Home," the *U.S.S. Lt. Boyce* plowing through flower-
strewn Manila Bay, headed out to sea . . . our boys were going
home.

Chapter Nine

⚜ MY FIRST CHRISTMAS in tropical Manila promised to be a bleak one. There were no Christmas trees, except in the mountains far to the north over roads which were inaccessible even to Adam. And even if I had had a tree, there would be no trimmings. A few of the American wives had foreseen this situation and had brought along little imitation trees complete with trimmings. But obviously I could not have carried one on the "Sacred Carabao."

As the Yuletide season drew near, I assured myself again and again that I didn't need a Christmas Tree; to be living in this strange and beautiful land was compensation enough. We would just hang a Christmas Star in the window. Anyway, in the Philippines a star is used instead of a tree. In this tropical land these stars are beautifully constructed of five-pointed bamboo frames, covered with bright-colored tissue paper. Some are very large, perhaps four or five feet in diameter; others are so tiny they look like stars in a night sky. Suspended from the lower points of these stars are streamers which represent rays of light. During the Christmas Season there is a Christmas Star in the window of every Philippine home; they bring to the people the same message as the star which guided the Wise Men . . . Peace on Earth, Good Will toward Men.

Often, the business buildings have rows and rows of stars or Christmas lanterns hanging across their fronts for decoration. It is a beautiful and an unforgettable sight. Before the Yuletide, the vendors peddle the Christmas stars; this, too, is a colorful sight. They are carried on long bamboo poles, yoke-like, over their shoulders and on each end are rows and rows of these many-colored decorations.

Doy Laurel drove down in his new little foreign car, bringing a lovely star for Harvel. Doy never failed to call on us on holidays to bring greetings. Ramón Magsaysay came down to bring holiday greetings and three Christmas stars, one for each of us.

Our little quonset by the sea took on a gay holiday mood, and all was well until the day before Christmas, when I turned on the radio and from the army station came the voice of Bing Crosby singing "I'm Dreaming of a White Christmas." I burst into tears and sobbed so loudly that Josie hastened to my side, only to find I was just homesick to see a snow-covered blue spruce back in my beloved New Mexico.

I simply had to have a Christmas tree. I looked out of the window and all I saw was a tall papaya tree and a number of banana trees. The papaya leaves were so high that I could not reach them, so I gathered an armful of broad banana leaves. I tied them together and placed them in a little fish pot, the way you plant a blue spruce in a bucket filled with dirt. I took the butcher knife and shredded the broad leaves hoping they might look like pine needles, but I was only kidding myself. They resembled, more, the droopy ears of a sick rabbit.

Nevertheless, it was a tree of sorts, so I made it ready for Christmas. I wrapped a sheet around the fish pot and looked about for decorations. We had no pop corn, no bits of red ribbon, not even cards, for the Christmas mail had not arrived from the States.

Then I spied our little tree orchids, each growing on a piece of tree bark, their native habitat. They were just beginning to burst into bloom and by morning they would have a million little flowers that would look like tiny white butterflies. I gathered up three large sprays and nestled them in the branches of my banana-leafed tree.

I collected a few gifts: two batangas (native knives), a small bottle of Cashmere Bouquet toilet water, and a beautiful fan from Spain, of the kind that are opened and closed with such a flourish.

When Huddy and Harvel came in that evening, they both looked at the funny contraption on the window seat and asked why on earth I wanted to abuse the little tree orchids. Didn't I know they thrived better in the sun room?

I had a hard time convincing them that the object was a Christmas Tree, but together we laughed about my effort. We went to bed to await the dawn, for then we would have a Christmas Tree trimmed in white orchids. Did a queen ever have such a royal Christmas?

At two o'clock in the morning we were aroused with a loud rapping at the door. The guard from the American Embassy was "Paul Revering" the compound, warning us to run for our lives to the Embassy Building, for "Jeanne" would strike at any minute and our lives were in danger. Jeanne was a typhoon.

We had lived through other typhoons. There was "Beverly." The navy boys had sighted her off northern Luzon and reported she was quite a gal. She, too, wore a billowing blue skirt and a petticoat trimmed with a thousand frills. She frolicked around in the China Sea, rocking ships as if they were cradles, and sent seasoned old seamen to the rails. She was headed, so the navy boys said, for Manila, but got tangled with the head hunters in northern Luzon and it was reported the Igorots lassoed her with a G-string. So we didn't see Beverly.

There was "Gertrude." That husky lass came in with a huff and a puff. She even closed the American School and surrounded the building with four feet of water. Oh yes, we had seen many of these devilish girls—there were "Dora," "Kathy," and "Pauline." But Jeanne, with the sea weed in her hair, promised to be the most wicked that ever swished a foamy-edged petticoat in the China Sea. And she had chosen Christmas Night to lash us.

The family took one look at the funny little tree, grabbed JoJo, gathered up the girls, and all of us ran for shelter. The occupants of the other twenty-nine huts in the compound were also running for shelter. As we rushed into the dignified Embassy Building, dragging along pet monkeys, dogs, cats, and canaries, we must have resembled the group that entered Noah's Ark.

For seven hours Jeanne tantalized us. We could see housetops go sailing through the air; large pieces of sheet metal fluttered like scraps of paper; huge branches of acacia trees beat against the walls; and from the bay, ships with lost anchors came bounding toward the sea wall. Christmas was forgotten. We only hoped our own quonset on stilts had withstood this first lashing. Suddenly all was calm. Jeanne had passed over.

We wended our way through the rubbish to our little home. The papaya trees were broken, the banana trees stripped of their leaves, and the orchids from the sun porch were far out in the bay.

Our quarters were drenched. The little fish pot was broken, the sheet soggy, the funny little tree toppled over. The Cashmere Bouquet was spilled and no one would ever again open and close the little Spanish fan with a flourish . . . but amidst the débris, the little butterfly orchids, so used to the mountain storms, had burst out in a million white blossoms.

It was Christmas Day. Tenderly I caressed a spray of tiny flowers, and standing there in a drenched quonset hut, in a land where a snow flake had never fallen, our family sang: "I'm Dreaming of a White Christmas."

Chapter Ten

⁂ THE DOCTOR had received orders from Washington to proceed to Zambales and examine an ailing veteran in order to expedite his claim in the adjudication department. He made the trip on a Saturday, and since the Legislature was not in session on this day, asked Ramón Magsaysay to accompany him since this was Ramón's home province and the veteran had been a "Magsaysay Guerrilla."

Huddy knew I loved the barrio life, so I was permitted to go along. Ramón arrived at six o'clock dressed in his khaki trousers and wearing a red-flowered shirt. He carried a small khaki bag, the overnight type used by the air force. I assumed he planned to spend the night in his province.

I sat in the front of the jeep with Tony. Huddy and Ramón occupied the rear seat. As we drove through the barrios, Ramón was hailed by all who saw him. We stopped long enough for him to visit a farmer in a rice paddy. We met a funeral procession. In the provinces it is a familiar sight to see the coffin carried by friends down the road to the cemetery with the mourners following on foot. Ramón got out of the jeep to shake hands with everyone. The pall bearers placed the casket on the ground to shake his hand. He was their congressman fighting for their needs.

It was a very hot day. Huddy's khaki shirt was so wet it stuck to his back; Ramón's flowered shirt was also limp. When we stopped at a gasoline station to have the jeep serviced, Ramón picked up the khaki bag and disappeared. When we were ready to leave, here came Ramón looking very refreshed. I glanced at him, then asked: "Ramón, am I seeing things? When we left Manila your shirt was covered with red flowers. Now they are blue. Are you a chameleon?"

"I always carry a change of shirts in this little bag, and I often change my shirt two or three times a day, especially on long jaunts."

When we reached Castillejos, Ramón went about the town greeting old friends. It had been in this town that the Japanese placed a bounty on his head: a reward of 100,000 pesos for the capture of Ramón Magsaysay, dead or alive. He was enemy number one. And yet not a single Filipino ever thought of turning him in for the reward.

The Doctor and I arrived at the nipa hut of the veteran. We climbed a bamboo ladder to reach the room where he lay on a straw mat. The man was very ill. Huddy examined him, gave him medication for temporary relief, and ordered him into a Manila hospital for treatment. Huddy always took plenty of time to sit and visit with a patient. He believed a doctor's friendly visit was often better therapy than pills.

As we sat with the patient, we learned of his great respect and devotion for Ramón Magsaysay. The patient was a survivor of a thirty-five member guerrilla band which had staged an ambush on a Japanese convoy to clear the way for General MacArthur's march to Manila. The General had landed his invasion forces at Lingayen Gulf on January 9, 1945. The ambush was unsuccessful, and fourteen of the thirty-five guerrillas under Captain Eduardo Johnson were killed and many others wounded, including this veteran. Ramón Magsaysay, the patient told us, wept when he learned of the death of his men, and it was Ramón who buried them. He went to a farmer and borrowed a cart into which he placed the bodies of the dead. He dug a common grave, using only his army knife and a large bolo knife. Then, gently lifting each dead comrade onto his own broad shoulders, he carried each body to the grave, and lowered it gently into its last resting place in the Luzon jungle. He gathered ferns and petals of flowers which he scattered over the bodies before the grave was filled.

Ramón Magsaysay was a gentle person, yet he could be a roaring lion. For instance, one time after he had assumed his duties as congressman from Zambales, a politician called upon him in his ramshackle office—the legislature building was still in ruins—and tried to make a deal. No one could make a deal with Ramón Magsaysay! He gave the man a briefing that was an ear-splitter, and to emphasize his point, swung his fist at the wall with such violence, the wall came tumbling down.

It was late in the day when we left Zambales, and by this time Ramón was wearing a bright pink shirt! He was unusually quiet as we drove along, for he was concerned with the plight of his neighbors. Many of them were boys who had served in his own ragged little army.

"The boys fought so hard, they have done one so much for their country, we owe them so much. But what can I do for them? What can I do?" He was emotionally upset.

Huddy patted his shoulder: "Ramón, my boy, let me tell you what to do. You run for president of the Philippines. Then, when you are in Malagañang Palace, you can solve the problems of your people." That remark cheered Ramón. He and Huddy had a good laugh at such a far-fetched suggestion.

The Doctor was off on an inspection trip of the Provincial Hospitals in Mindanao. The U.S. Government had a supply of medical equipment in the Philippines that was now declared surplus. It was the Doctor's assignment to visit these hospitals and to assign hospital equipment where he decided it was most needed. Before his departure, he had been briefed by the Com-

manding Officer on the dangers of a trip deep into the heart of
Moroland. The C.O. would send along a bodyguard, and the
Doctor should select the fire-arms he would need.

Huddy, much to the disgust of the C.O., had armed himself
with bottles of aspirin, quinine, Atabrine, and with cigarettes and
chocolate bars. He had resembled a vagabond peddler as he
boarded a navy plane for Davao, his first stop.

Harvel and I took off by plane for Zamboanga to meet Huddy.
Flying over the 7,000 islands that make up the archipelago was
no luxury trip, but it was an exciting one. In the old days, the
people traveled by boat or vinta, a small skiff, but since the
islands have been linked with a network of airways, they ride
the planes as Americans do Greyhound buses.

Harvel and I arrived at the airport dressed in black linen suits,
matching hats, sandals, and leis of sweet sampaguita around our
necks. The airport was crowded. A barefoot woman, smoking a
black cigar hind-part before, shouldered two stalks of sugar cane,
at least four inches in diameter and six feet long; another carried
a basket of smelly dried fish; others had pigs in baskets and coops
of squawking chickens. The passengers had to wait until the
chickens were loaded, since they are placed in the rear of the
bucket-seated plane.

I sat next to a man whose bare feet rested on a bamboo crate
in which was a pig that squealed louder and louder as the plane
soared higher in the air. To my left was seated the woman with
the sugar cane which she now held upright in front of her. The
stalks would slide my way and jab at my head. I had to hold on to
my linen chapeau, otherwise it would be modeled by a stalk of
sugar cane. Finally the aged woman took a balisong knife out of
her pocket, whacked off a couple of joints of the cane and ate it
for her lunch. That shortened a stalk and I could sit more comfortably.

The pilot asked the woman with the basket of smelly fish to
remove it to the rear, for the odor was so obnoxious. She was

agreeable and made her way to the rear of the plane, and set the basket amidst the coops of chickens. They started squawking and flapping their wings. The feathers flew about the plane and we batted them out of our faces as we winged on to Cebu City.

The island of Cebu is very mountainous, but we landed safely and discharged many passengers, among them the woman with the stalks of cane, and the man with the pig. Others with baskets of produce boarded the plane.

At Dumaguete, on the island of Negroes, we landed in a cornfield. The stalks were higher than a man's head, in full golden tassel. Tall coconut trees were the immediate background, and projected against them were nipa huts with blooming flowers in the windows and bright-colored laundry on the bamboo fences to dry. In the distances, the mountaintops were tangled with clouds. The countryside, rinsed with a fresh shower, had a good sweet smell. As I stepped off the plane, I saw the new and the old, side by side: an old carratela drawn by a dwarfish pony and a brand-new Ford car.

The airport terminal was a quonset hut. I shall always argue that the quonset huts in the post-war Philippines should be lauded: they were used for churches, hospitals, schools, mortuaries, residences, and businesses.

It took skill to land the plane at Dipolog, but we landed on the beach with not an inch to spare. I could have dipped up water with my left hand, and plucked a coconut with my right hand, for the coconut grove reached almost to the water's edge. The Doctor had flown in from Cotabato and was waiting on the beach to witness this spectacular landing, for it is truly a feat and one that only a skilled pilot could accomplish.

Then we were off to Zamboanga—that paradise by the Sulu Sea, the land where the monkeys have no tails, the land of the "Juramentado." Just a sprawling sleepy Spanish village dreaming by the sea, yet it is the largest incorporated city in the world. It

even takes in Basilan Island across Basilan Strait and has miles
and miles of unexplored jungle.

We were greeted at the plane by the J. S. Johnson family,
whom Huddy had met, and given a sightseeing trip before we
were taken to our hotel. We drove up Ramón Highway toward
the Penal Colony. This fabulous highway, made of pure white
coral, follows the very edge of the water and glistens in the late
evening sun like a snow-covered road.

The Sulu Sea, a pure cobalt blue, was picturesque with a
fleet of Moro vintas skimming along. A dense coconut grove
follows Ramón Highway . . . happy trees, because it is said a
coconut tree cannot thrive unless it hears the murmur of the sea.

When we returned from our drive, the setting sun had turned
the sky a red and orange; even the highway had turned a rosy
hue. The Sulu Sea was now red, and the white trunks of the
coconut trees, turned pink, resembled a flock of flamingos. We
met a little boy wearing a pink shirt, riding on the broad back
of a carabao; even the leathery skin of the animal had taken on
a mauve hue.

The nipa huts at Zamboanga are very elaborate. The open
windows displayed baskets of ferns and potted plants of many
colors. I do not recall that I ever saw a blue-colored flower in
the Philippines. Perhaps the blue of the sea and the blue of the
sky will have no copy-cats.

Zamboanga is clean swept. There is no hurry, no mad traffic,
no horn tooting. Just a slow-moving life, as if the people were so
content they wanted the days not to run out too quickly.

The Moros on the streets were very colorful in cotton Samal
pants which were loose and full and caught at the ankles like a
clown's suit. Their favorite colors are red, orange, and yellow, but
I saw costumes of green, purple, blue, and even black. Many of
the men still wear their hair long, tied in a knot, and all darken
their teeth and their lips a brilliant red with the juice of the
betel nuts which they chew constantly.

The name Moro was applied to this race of hardy, self-willed people by the Spaniards because six out of the twenty-three tribal groups inhabiting this region were of the Mohammedan faith. The remainder are tribal people, among whom is to be found a group of Christians.

Mohammedanism in the Philippine Islands was introduced by adventurers who came to Mindanao and Sulu from Borneo and Malacca toward the beginning of the Fifteenth Century during the latter period of the Javanese Empire of Majapahit, of which these islands were formerly political dependencies. After the fall of that empire, the Mohammedan states of Maguindanao, on the island of Mindanao, and of Sulu, in the islands of the southwestward, came into their own. They were actually first known toward the end of the Fifteenth Century and were discovered for the Western World by Magellan in 1521.

The very first rulers of these states were Arab-Malay nobles, members of the royal families of Borneo and Malacca. They married daughters of the native rulers and, in emphasis of their religious affiliations, gave to themselves the title of "sultan," as distinguished from the title of "rajah" which had been used by the native kings. And from this line, so established, the families have continued. In 1918 the Sultan of Maguindanao was the twenty-first, and that of Sulu, the twenty-fifth, of their respective lines.

The story goes that one or two Mohammedan missionaries had preceded the arrival of those who set themselves up as the first sultans, and the teachings of these missionaries had greatly contributed to the ease with which the sultans made their conquests. The Mohammedan missionary is self-sustaining, usually by trade, and there is no organized financial support for foreign missions. The missionary is accorded great respect, since he works among people he considers of inferior civilization and he generally claims to be an Arab and a descendant of the Prophet. As early as the Fifteenth Century, missionaries introduced the art of writing in Mindanao, adapting the Arabic alphabet to Malay Phonetics. Arabic and Malay books on law and religion were translated into the native dialects.

By the year 1565, the beginning of the Spanish conquest, Mohammedan adventurers and traders, chiefly from Borneo, had established themselves at points on the coast and had extended their religion as far north as Manila. The religion had been established for a longer period in the southern islands, but it had not been generally accepted. The majority of the inhabitants of the island of Mindanao were still pagan.

Even after the occupation of Luzon and the Visayas by the Spaniards, the Sultan of Borneo continued his efforts to maintain and extend Mohammedanism in those islands. In 1578, the Spaniards made a successful military expedition to Borneo and eradicated Mohammedanism from all the Philippine Islands southward from Luzon through the Visayan Islands and practically the entire north and east coasts of Mindanao. Then, for nearly three hundred years, the Spaniards made no sustained campaign against the Moros and occupied no permanent strategic places, except Zamboanga at the southwestern point of Mindanao.

Mohammedans in the Philippines may be divided generally into the following main groups: the Maguindanaos in the Cotabato Valley; the Maranaos in the Lake Lanao region; the Yakans on the island of Basilan; the Samals on the coast of the peninsula of Zamboanga and throughout the islands to the southward of Mindanao. Though there is no recognized caste system among these people, the Samals are regarded by the Moros as of inferior standing.

There is a very extraordinary group of rovers, known as Bajaos, who move between Borneo and the Philippine Islands, living on boats and called "Sea Gypsies." They are a very timid race and engage exclusively in fishing. They are pagan in religion, having never embraced the Mohammedan faith. The Mohammedans hold them in utter contempt.

The long-haired Bajaos are not a warring tribe; they live and die on their boats at sea. Sometimes, when they come ashore, they get "land legs" and can't walk and become violently landsick. The Bajaos move about to find shelter from the wind. There are colonies of these floating homes with a population of from two to five thousand people. If a boat is wrecked by a storm, the entire colony helps to make a new one; if one family lacks food, the others will help out; if a child is left alone through the death of its parents, some other boat family will care for it. Births, weddings, and funerals are all experienced on these floating homes of the Bajaos.

Bajaos build their own homes, for they are master boat builders. They use a tree trunk as the basis for many types of boats, including the vinta, the sapit, and the lipa. The lipa is larger and roomier than the vinta; it is used by the poorer class as living quarters.

The wealthy Bajaos live in boat houses which are carved from a treelog fifty feet long and five feet across. Erected on top of this boat is a crude house, often ten feet wide and thirty feet long. These boats are put together without nails or screws and often are beautifully carved with a bolo knife. The wealthy Bajaos live in elaborate boat houses that remain in the harbor. They have a vinta tied to the boat house which is used for fishing or to go visiting a neighbor.

I wanted to see an elaborate Bajao boat house, for many were harbored at Zamboanga. I wanted to visit a Samal fishing village nearby, built out over the water, as are all Moro villages. But I had to wait. I was to accompany my husband into the province to inspect a provincial hospital. Harvel was not feeling very well, so she remained at the hotel.

We started out early in the morning. Huddy carried a supply of Atabrine tablets, cigarettes, and chocolate bars. Atabrine was very scarce and sold on the black market at a price prohibitive to the Filipinos, so they had to suffer with chills and fever and were often too sick to work in the rice paddies. Many of them had no word for Atabrine; to them it was a little yellow pill that relieved malaria. As we traveled deep into the provinces, the word spread by bamboo telegraph that the Doctor was due to arrive in a certain barrio. The sick and weary would hurry down the road to meet him—on foot, by bull cart, and by calesa. When they sighted the army jeep coming around the coconut grove, a cry went up: "The Yellow Doctor is coming!" "The Yellow Doctor is coming!" It was a complimentary title, but I was thankful the pill was yellow and not red.

The mob would descend upon him, stretching out thin, feverish hands for a few Atabrine tablets. With this medication they would feel better and could return to the rice fields. Who had need of a gun?

We arrived at the Provincial Hospital, or what was left of it. This particular location had been looted, bombed, and burned by the Japanese, and the hospital destroyed. The Philippine doctors and nurses, with the help of the Red Cross, had erected an emergency building with bamboo walls and floors and a thatched roof made of coconut leaves. It was an open-air building with neither windows nor screens.

The equipment of this crude hospital consisted of donated U.S. army cots with one blanket each. There were no bed sheets and no mattresses, nor were there facilities for blood testing or urinalysis. There was no kind of laboratory equipment available; the nearest X-Ray machine was a small unit some 300 miles away. There was no means of refrigeration for the perishable foods. The scant diet was prepared under the shade of a huge mango tree while the houseboys constantly swished large banana leaves in a vain effort to keep the flies out of the food.

I went with my husband to make rounds. We walked amidst unbelievable squalor and visited patients who lay suffering on cots placed side by side with a mere foot of space between them. When all of the cots were filled, other sick and injured were placed on straw mats on the floor.

I shall never forget one room in which twenty patients were crowded—a ward that ordinarily would accommodate not over six people. The only toilet facility was an outdoor, unscreened privy about 100 yards away, and if a patient was unable to walk the distance, then it was necessary that he use an open bucket on the floor beside his cot.

The doctors and nurses and the Red Cross made valiant efforts to render all possible aid. The head physician, a Philippine doctor, who had accompanied us on our rounds, pleaded with my husband, in hopes that through this American doctor some help might come. "Oh, sir, can't you see the pitiful plight of these poor people, and the conditions under which we are trying to work? We have practically no medicine and you can see the facilities. Oh, God, if your government could only help us! To ask our government for help at this time would be like praying for snow in the Philippines."

Thank heaven, Doctor Huddleston was able to assure him help was forthcoming. As Huddy and I left the hospital, we faced a group of people waiting outside to see a nurse or a doctor, or to receive whatever meager medical care could be given them. Near the front door stood a woman with a little boy about five years old. She was gaunt and emaciated, and the little boy was pitifully undernourished. The Doctor reached in his coat pocket for a chocolate bar and handed it to the little boy. The grateful mother placed her hand on his arm and said: "Please, dear doctor, my little Alberto he wants so much a song for you to sing." We listened appreciatively while the ragged, pot-bellied Alberto burst forth in clear childish tones with "God Bless America."

The next day, Harvel and I set out on foot for one of the Moro villages built on stilts out in the water. As we neared it, a group of little Moro boys came running to meet us to act as our guides. They were as naked as jay birds, but had strong, brown bodies and were completely unconscious of their nakedness. I could see the vintas skimming through the water, then an elaborately carved house boat moving along; on deck a Moro wife was hanging out a washing. The village was some three hundred yards out in the water. The thatch-roofed huts were elevated on bamboo pilings about six feet above the water. To gain entrance to the village, we had to walk a rickety gangplank made of several thick bamboo poles wired together.

We removed our sandals to accomplish this feat, as our little guides had instructed us to grab the poles with our toes so we wouldn't totter. A crowd of youngsters came running across to meet us. The bamboo bridge swayed with the weight of so many that I was fearful it might break and dump us in the Sulu Sea. The little boys all dived into the water and we tossed pennies to them. They dived like fish and brought up the pennies between their teeth.

Around the Moro village the children played in the water as our American children play on a grassy lawn. I watched a very old woman come to the door, leap into the water fully clothed and paddle over to another hut. The neighbor sat in her doorway and talked to the aged one who gracefully tread water while she carried on a conversation—like two American housewives hanging over the backyard fence. The visit ended, and the old woman paddled back to her nipa hut and climbed up a ladder.

A woman wearing a colorful Moro costume came to her door and called out: "Come on, Americans, you are welcome!" and a dozen Moro women were at the end of this makeshift bridge to give us a hand. The beautifully dressed Moro invited us into her house and promised to dance for us. We followed her over another shaky bamboo bridge, but a shorter one this time, to her house, which was the very last one projecting out over the Sulu Sea.

Just as we were about to enter, we sighted a procession of boats
flying gay colors, with a group on deck beating gongs and doing
a primitive dance. In the midst of the group stood a couple—a
girl with her face painted white, and the boy beside her with
his face painted the same way. The crowd on the boat wore
gay-colored sarongs, and banners and flags were flying. When
they started beating the side of the boat with spears I was
frightened. "Don't pay any attention to them," said our hostess.
"They are Bajaos; they are pagans. It is just a wedding party; the
girl and the boy with the white faces have just been married."

Our hostess politely stepped aside so that we might enter
her house. The room was very clean. There was an iron bed-
stead and over the mattress was a chenille bedspread of bright
yellow, likely an order from Sears Roebuck; an old trunk and a
sewing machine completed the furnishings. We sat on the bed
as she had asked us to do.

"I shall do for you a Moro dance," she said. With the grace
and the poise of a professional, she interpreted the dance of her
tribe. The Moro hut was a stage and she was a Margot Fonteyn,
a Martha Graham, a Taos Indian. She was lightning; she was
the gentle rain; she was a breeze from the Sulu Sea. When she
finished her dance, she sat next to me on the bed and in excellent English, explained it. We gave her pesos and she danced
again. Soon the room was filled with little boys and girls dancing
for us, and we would toss coins to them. But the hostess, in her
native tongue, banished them from the room, then sidled over
to be and asked: "You buy my cat's eyes?"

"Cat's eyes"—not to be confused with the semi-precious quartz
gem—are shells, larger and thicker than a five cent piece. The
Moros gather these shells on the beaches. This area is included
in the Indo-Pacific Province, the largest and richest shell region
in the world, which extends from the shores of East Africa
through the East Indies to Polynesia.

"Cat's eyes" have a texture like mother of pearl with dark

green coloring in the center. They are used for buttons and often fashioned in necklaces and rings. The cat's eyes found in this region come from turban shell, a marine snail, which is a herbivorous species of South Pacific coral reefs. The beautiful cat's eyes serve as trap doors which close the shell when the animal retracts.

The Moro woman opened an old trunk and took out a cigar box filled with the largest and most perfect cat's eyes I had ever seen. I held one that was fully an inch in diameter in my hand. She told me the price was ten pesos. I thought she was pricing the cat's eye I held in my hand. In Manila a good cat's eye sold for one peso. "Too high," I said.

"Very well, my American friend, you may have them for eight pesos."

I hesitated. Then she shoved the cigar box toward me. "It is not too dear. There are many cat's eyes in the box." She let them spill through her fingers to convince me they were worth the price.

Eight pesos for a box of cat's eyes! I must not appear too anxious. I, too, fingered through the stones as I calculated their value on the Manila market. Yet I must not delay too long. She might change her mind. So I said: "My friend, I will pay you ten pesos for the box of cat's eyes." She took the money and handed over the box.

I shall never know how I made it over the rickety bamboo bridge with my treasure, for I was in a great hurry. I had a guilty feeling as if I had robbed the woman of the cat's eyes and deserved to fall into the Sulu Sea.

When I was safely in my hotel room I emptied the box on my bed and Harvel and I counted the cat's eyes. Ninety five! Quickly I did my arithmetic—the value in Manila would be that many pesos? I locked the shells in my overnight case as if I were hiding them from the law. Harvel said I should not feel guilty for I had actually paid the woman two pesos more than her asking price. And so I had.

We set out for the market place in Zamboanga hoping to find other bargains. I bought a hat right off the head of a Moro who even tried to sell me the earrings from his ears. We were loaded with mats, bracelets, and hats when we came upon Fenton Carbine from Manila. The government had sent him down in the interest of U.S. Fish and Wildlife. Fenton was excited, for he had just seen the wife of a Datu Chieftain—she wore a long silk robe fastened from chin to ankles with buttons made of twenty-dollar gold pieces. It was a fabulous gown, so he said.

Harvel and I just had to see such a garment. The three of us rushed back to the market stall to find the woman. Perhaps we came upon her too suddenly, or perhaps our American ways were too bold, at any rate, when Fenton started to finger the gold buttons on her gown she screamed, then dashed away in fright. The three of us took off in the opposite direction.

As I watched this full-breasted Moro woman race away, I wondered if she might be the one who had been offered the week before to share my husband's bed. The Doctor had been on an inspection trip south of Davao and had been entertained in the home of a Datu. After the evening meal, the Datu clapped his hands, and soon appeared his four wives. Under the Mohammedan religion, plural marriages are permitted and practiced by Sultans, Datus, and Maharajahs. If they are very wealthy, they may have many wives.

The four wives who appeared before my husband wore elaborate Moro costumes and were bedecked with jewels. Their teeth and lips were stained a deep red with betel nuts. The women bowed before the Datu and his guest; then they filed by, each carefully eyeing my husband. "Doctor," said the Datu, "You will be my guest for the night. Which one of my wives do you wish to share your bed?" In Moroland this was an act of hospitality, but Huddy—so *his* story goes—found an excuse to hurry back to Davao.

Fenton and I went over to the sea wall to watch the colorful vintas out in the Sulu Sea while Harvel went off on a shopping jaunt. I had just finished telling Fenton about my cat's eyes bargain when I felt a hand on my shoulder. I turned, half expecting to face the old Datu whose wife we had frightened. Instead, I looked into the angry face of a Moro. "My wife dance for you this morning?" he asked. "Yes." I answered, still remembering the grace of her body.

"You buy cat's eyes out of my trunk. Much too cheap. I want them back."

"Oh," I replied. "It wasn't I. It was the other woman," meaning Harvel, who at this moment was bargaining with a Moro over his earrings.

"Go get her," he demanded.

Just then I sighted a plane rising in the air, headed for Manila. "She's gone. She's on that plane." I said. Just at that moment we saw Harvel coming toward us, waving the earrings. While Fenton went to delay her, I made rash promises to the Moro. I would certainly find that "cat's eyes thief" when I returned to Manila.

I thought it best not to tell the Doctor about the cat's eyes— he was so honest he would march me over that little bamboo bridge at midnight to make me return the shells. The next day we were to go across to Basilan Island to spend the weekend with Don Robinson, the Coconut King of Zamboanga. I would ask Don what I should do, for I was still conscience-stricken.

A large Moro vinta with sails of black and yellow stood at the pier to carry us across the Basilan Strait to the Robinson plantation. I was excited, for the vinta reminded me of a pirate ship, but my enthusiasm was short-lived. When I stepped into the vinta, I came face to face with the head boatman—the Moro whose cat's eyes were now in my possession. He glowered at me and was very sullen as he headed the gay craft across the bay. The other boatman was a very friendly Moro who pointed out the beds of black coral in the Sulu Sea. This rare coral is fashioned into bracelets and rings.

As I stepped ashore on Basilan Island, the Moro stalked up to me and said in an angry voice: "Give me back my cat's eyes." Don Robinson walked up at this moment, and sensing a disagreement, gave the Moro a good dressing down; he sullenly retreated. When I told Don about the cat's eyes purchase, he informed me I had paid five pesos too much. The Moro was very lucky to get ten pesos for the shells. I felt much better and consoled myself that the Moros had skinned the daylights out of me!

Don's Yakan Plantation was a 2,700-acre estate, eight miles from Lamitan. Don, in partnership with William Saner of Dallas, had established this plantation over forty years before. It was the dream of many Americans who lingered for a spell in the islands to some day own such a place.

The Coconut King of Zamboanga had graduated from the University of Texas School of Law back in 1906. At the turn of the century Don Robinson had captained the great football team at Texas University and had become nationally known as a gridiron star. After graduating, he went to work as a U.S. Government engineer in Hawaii and the Philippines. He returned to the States and married Ann Hodges of Dallas, a talented violinist and concert mistress for Dallas' first Symphony Orchestra. The bride shared her husband's desire to return to the islands and promote the coconut plantation, and for many years the couple lived in the lap of luxury in this far away paradise beside Sulu Sea.

At the outbreak of the war, the Robinsons rigged up a little house-boat similar to the ones used by the Bajaos and made their way up the east coast of the Zamboanga peninsula. Here they abandoned the boat and penetrated deep into the jungle where they remained hidden until after The Liberation. The very day they were to set out on this expedition, Don received a wire from the War Department; their son Bill had been killed in action. He tore up the telegram, simply returned to the house, and continued packing up a few articles to take with them on their journey. For three long years he kept locked in his heart this heart-breaking secret, in order that Ann, who was in frail health, might better survive the long trek.

During their years of hiding from the Japanese, the coveted violin was carried along with the meager provisions. There was to be many a concert deep in the jungles, and Ann Robinson and her violin made life a bit easier for her husband and the few friends who shared their hideout.

War ended. The Robinsons returned to their plantation, and like everyone else, started to rebuild. Soon they were reestablished and set up open house for the American G.I. In 1946 they returned to the States because Ann Robinson's health was failing; this was Don's first trip back home in thirty years. He returned shortly to the islands and left his wife in Dallas on account of her health.

At the time of our visit, Don had the plantation once more in full copra production. He was getting things in shape to sell out and return to Dallas, because his wife could no longer live in the Orient.

The plantation was a beauty spot. The elaborate house was built of sawali, woven bamboo slats. We sat on the spacious veranda which was filled with ferns and orchids, and the fragrance of gardenias permeated the air. Don clapped his hands and his houseboy appeared to take his order for coconut milk. The boy returned with a large bamboo tray which held green coconuts with the tops slashed off. Tiny butterfly orchids floated on the ice-cold coconut milk. This was a luxury I had never dreamed would come my way. At this moment I felt like a Queen of the Orient.

As we sipped the drink, Don spoke of the Moros. These were

TO THE PHILIPPINES WITH LOVE

a strange people, but good-hearted, trying hard to live and to let live. They wanted no interference with their religion, Mohammedanism, and were ready to leave the Christian to his own brand of worship.

I wanted to hear about the "Juramentado." Before we left Manila, José had been concerned about our safety. "Mom" said he, "Watch out for a juramentado." I told José that the gory stories about juramentados had happened in the long ago. But I was mistaken, for he handed me the morning paper (although he himself could not yet read) with this headline: "A Juramentado runs amok. Three people are killed on the streets of Zamboanga."

Don Robinson briefed us about them: a Moro's religion teaches that should he meet death as a result of killing a Christian (or going "Juramentado") he will go to paradise. So, when a Moro becomes tired of life, or perhaps disappointed in a love affair, he will go juramentado. He shaves his eyebrows, is blessed by one of his own priests, puts on a snow-white garment, and rushes out to kill as many Christians as he can before meeting his own death. A juramentado will sneak up on his intended victim and wait for a chance when he can rush in and start slashing at him with a kris.

In the old days, should a Moro run amok and be sighted, there went up a cry: "Juramentado! Juramentado!" and folk ran to get out of the path of the assailant. Don Robinson related a thrilling tale. He and his wife were in Zamboanga for a day. They were strolling down the streets when suddenly a cry pierced the air: "Juramentado!" They knew they must get out of the path of the death-crazed Moro! Don's eyes scanned a tall coconut tree as a possible means of escape; he thought of their running toward the sea and leaping over the sea wall; or should they jump into a passing calesa? Yes, that would be a means of escape! He turned quickly to grab his wife's arm; she was not there. He looked about for her headless body . . . then he heard her voice. "Don, run for your life!", and there on top of the bank building stood

Ann Robinson. How she had scaled the wall, he didn't know; nor did she. At any rate, she escaped the juramentado's gleaming kris.

In the month of September is observed "Hari-raya," the Moro's equivalent of our Christmas. Hari-raya, the biggest holiday of the year, is preceded by "pausa," a thirty-day period of penitence which is observed with fasting. Among other special holidays which precede the fasting period is "maulud," the day the Moros celebrate the birth of the Moslem prophet, Mohammed; also "mispu," the day decreed for the visiting of graves. This is the equivalent of our All Souls Day. During Hari-raya the Sultan reigns supreme. He holds the biggest "Noche Buena," and at this time the people hand over to him their sundry share of the celebration: cash, cattle, staple foods, or the like.

The ritual is one of ancient pageantry. The common people who have brought an offering feel it is their duty to kiss the hand of the Sultan, since it is Hari-raya. But the Sultan, swathed in an elaborate costume, sits on a decorated throne which is so high, common people can't touch him. He is surrounded by high priests, fakirs, and other religious attendants, all ceremoniously gowned. They gather in the spacious palace to intone and chant prayers for the spiritual pilgrimage to Mecca, now about to get under way. Just before midnight, this ceremony ends. At six o'clock, a Hari-raya mass is held in the community mosque.

Now their "Christmas" starts. The entire community turns out to celebrate. Homes are decorated with palm leaves and paper lanterns of every color and shape. It is an eerie fairyland. Men, women, and children are in festive garb. However, a Moro woman is never on the streets, not even during Hari-raya, unless she is escorted by her husband, a son, or a relative. The happy, noisy children even forget to eat, except sweets which they buy with their pennies. Usually on this day the men spend the entire day at the cockpits or witness a spectacular bull fight.

When Don had finished his story of Hari-raya, the sun was

setting. The whole plantation took on a misty pink haze. He ordered his car and driver to take us deep into a coconut grove. He was going to prove to me "the monkeys have no tails in Zamboanga" (like in the title of the song). He sent one of the plantation workers shinnying up a tall tree to cut green coconuts. The man, with a huge bolo knife at his waist, clasped his hands around the trunk of the tree and simply walked to the top.

"There's your monkey." said Don. "That is where the expression comes from!" I did not appreciate the remark, and I told him so. It took training and physical endurance for the Moro to climb that tree. I looked on while he, at the top of the tree, locked his legs around its trunk, drew his bolo from his belt, and whacked off choice green coconuts. They fell at our feet with a thud, many of them bursting wide open like watermelons, with delicious milk spilling upon the ground. I ran from coconut to coconut to sip the milk left in the shells.

Apparently the man had bruised the tree, for when he slid to the ground, Don spoke in a brutal tone: "You black devil! I'll take that bolo and whack your damn head off!"

I noticed the sullen look on the Moro's face. He looked at Don's neck, then at the bolo in his belt, then from the bolo back to Don's neck. Then he slinked away like a dog that had been kicked. What was going on in his mind?

Don turned to Huddy and said: "Doctor, you've got to show 'em who's boss." And Don Robinson *was* the boss! He was the "Coconut King of Zamboanga." He was a genial man. He might speak crossly to a dozen men, yet there were one hundred others who worshipped him. Most of the help in his own household seemed to hold him in high esteem.

We left next day by Moro vinta for Zamboanga. Don Robinson stood on the pier to wave goodbye. Behind him was Basilan Island, the Yakan Moro tribe, and his own great coconut plantation; the dreamer and his dream. "I'll see you back in the States one day soon," he called out.

Not many moons had come and gone. We were back in Manila when over the wires came: "The Coconut King of Zamboanga murdered." Then the story broke. Don was murdered in cold blood by a Moro who was employed in the office store of his plantation at Lamitan, Basilan Island. The alleged killer was named Benson Masaganda. I shall never know if it was the man who had skinned up the coconut tree. Anyway, Masaganda, the murderer, had fired five shots from a carbine into Don Robinson's right side, killing him instantly. He had then escaped with the gun which had belonged to Don.

The story went that Masaganda, who had been a worker at the plantation, had been discharged several days previously by Don for stealing coconuts and for rustling cattle. The cashier at the office reported that two days before the murder the man had gone to Don and asked him to reconsider his decision and give him some food. Others said that the murderer had asked for money due him, but Don had refused to pay it until the theft charges were cleared.

Strange that again and again I recalled the man who had skinned up the coconut tree. Again and again I recalled Don's cruel words. Sooner or later that pent-up hatred in the Moro's heart would break loose. Then *he* would be the boss. A Moro with a bolo in his belt is not one to be antagonized.

No doubt Don Robinson, even though he was trying to do what was fair and right, had asked for his own death. I have often wondered if he had not said to Masaganda: "I'll take this carbine and pump five shots in your right side," not meaning it. But did he say it, thereby putting the very thought in the mind of the Moro? Did he? We'll never know.

Chapter Eleven

CEBU CITY WAS SCHEDULED for the Doctor's next inspection trip. As our plane neared its destination, we encountered an 80-mile-per-hour typhoon and were forced to detour to Bacolod, to try to make a landing. Even here, the pilot had to circle the town many times before we could land.

The rain was coming down in torrents. We ran for shelter in the small quonset hut, used as an air terminal. After the storm subsided, we inquired about hotel accommodations. A Philippine gentleman, whom we had never seen before, offered to drive us to Hotel Brisas del Mar, which had the best accommodations in town. We felt very luxurious in his new jeep station wagon as he took us for a short sight-seeing trip through the city. Our new friend turned out to be the manager of the Elizalde Sugar Company at Bacolod.

No sooner had we entered the hotel than a second typhoon struck with fury. Huddy, Harvel, and I stood on the glassed-in veranda and watched dozens of nipa huts turned upside down, their bamboo legs sticking up in the air, like cockroaches on their backs. The banana trees were stripped of their leaves and tall coconuts swayed, bent to the ground, and then snapped. The sea roared and heaved and small craft were washed up on the beaches. The window panes in the veranda were blown out, leaving splinters of glass over the floor. It was a dismal day; the night promised to be worse.

Our one room, with its "best accommodations," had not one stick of furniture except the mats on the floor. They were cold, damp, and hard. Cockroaches crawled over the floor and lizards over the ceiling. A big rat came through a hole in the wall and stood staring at us until Huddy chased him away. In the center of the room was a concrete post that rose up from the basement through a big hole in the floor. Just about the time we retired on our mats, there emerged through this opening a writhing rope of ants. This ant rope, at least six inches in diameter, was circling up the concrete post toward the ceiling. Many of the insects, unable to hold on, fell to the floor and were headed toward our mats. We backed into a corner of the room and screamed for help. A houseboy came to our rescue, and with twisted newspapers, which he set on fire, he used this makeshift torch to singe the ants until their charred bodies fell about the floor. He swept them up in a washtub and carried them away.

That was the longest night I ever experienced, and the most uncomfortable. I twisted and squirmed on the hard mat, half afraid another army of ants might decide to do a bit of pole climbing.

Dawn broke. The sea was calm and blue. Across the Bay of Guinas, the mountains stood out clear and majestic. These people take a typhoon in their stride. They set to rights their overturned nipa huts and are ready to face a new day. The beach was already crowded with men, women, and children gathering mussels. Now a friendly sea, it fed them and was forgiven for the tantrum it had thrown the night before.

I watched them wade far out into the water, pushing in front of them triangular-shaped fish nets stretched on bamboo frames; others rowed out in small bancas to cast their nets. The bull carts came down the beach and were driven right out into the sea to such a distance that only the driver's head and, it seemed, the horns of the carabao, were visible. Once loaded with fish, the bull cart returned to shore and was driven up the beach to market.

Later in the day, Dr. Jara and his wife, both Doctors of Medicine, came to call on us. Dr. Jara was in charge of a poorly equipped and bombed-out provincial hospital. He discussed with my husband the possibility of getting a small X-ray machine from an army surplus warehouse.

Dr. Jara will be remembered by all American civilians who were interned in Bacolod by the Japanese, for he was the official doctor who visited the Internment Camp. He called each day, and always the little black bag was bulging with bananas and other foods the Americans could not get inside the prison walls. As Thanksgiving drew near, the doctor emptied the bag of all medicine and stuffed it with a big fat turkey. He walked bravely past the Japanese guard. The next day and the next, he passed with a medicine bag that bulged to bursting point; on the fifth day, the guard eyed the bag a bit suspiciously.

"It is filled with castor oil." said Dr. Jara. "The damn Americans have plenty belly ache."

The guard, pleased with the predicament of the Americans and with Dr. Jara's proposed treatment, grinned as he let the castor oil bearer pass. There were five big turkeys for Thanksgiving.

We arrived in Cebu City the next day and went immediately to the post office to pick up orders from Manila, directing my husband on his next trip. The post office was housed in a shell-pocked, bombed-out building, yet there were traces to remind one of its former elaborate structure. The interior was partitioned into sections by the stacking of discarded, greasy oil barrels, one on top of the other, to form makeshift walls. We went to the general delivery window—this was made by omitting one barrel —to call for the Doctor's travel orders. Right then and there I wanted to doff my hat to the courageous Filipinos. In the days of reconstruction, the papers headlined thefts, greed, and looting, and the many who waxed rich overnight. And yet, the tens of thousands of brave, honest people working behind such greasy oil barrels as these never made the headlines.

Outside the post office, I bought a Chinese parasol for ten pesos. The vendor had many black umbrellas with strong handles, the kind the Filipinos use, but I chose a rose-colored parasol made of oilskin, for I am not a practical person.

The Doctor's travel orders directed him deep into the provinces where he was asked to examine an aged "pensionado" and make a report to the Veteran's Administration in Washington, D.C. He hired a car and a driver and we headed out. This trip was up toward Car-Car, one of the loveliest drives in the entire Philippines. We passed fields of corn in full tassel and acres and acres of sugar cane. We came upon a portland cement plant with a row of company houses, California style, completely out of place in this tropical region. For miles and miles we drove down a lane that was lined with tall acacia trees. The branches met overhead in an archway; it seemed we were driving under the great dome of a cathedral.

The banana trees grew luxuriantly. After this trip, I was fully convinced the Filipino could not carry on his daily life without the aid of a banana leaf. It had started to rain. When the barrio school dismissed, the children ran up the road carrying huge banana leaves over their heads in place of umbrellas. It gave the appearance of a banana grove walking down the middle of the road; an aged woman wore a folded leaf like a huge sunbonnet to keep the rain off her head. A bull cart loaded with green grasses was jogging down the road, and the little boy sitting on the rump of the carabao, held a banana leaf over his head; two little girls were riding sidewise on another old carabao and, they, too, used these native umbrellas.

We stopped at a botica to buy a soft drink, and the woman

wrapped a square of banana leaf around the bottle before she handed it to us. Inside a sari-sari, another woman was ironing. She wiped her iron over a banana leaf to give a rich sheen to the garments. We bought "puto" wrapped in a banana leaf.

As we journeyed on, we saw a jeep mired down in a corn field. We watched the men strip the banana trees and place the leaves under the wheels. And just like that, the driver was out of the mud! A blacksmith under a mango tree was hammering out a bolo knife. He wore an apron made of banana leaves.

Down the road, I sighted a woman with a large bamboo pole over her shoulder. The pole must have been six feet long with the circumference of a stove pipe.

"Look!" I exclaimed. "Did you ever see such a large fishing pole?"

Our driver laughed as he informed me it was a Filipino water bucket; when I looked again, I saw the water slosh out past the banana leaf tied over the end.

Car-Car is an interesting and colorful village with clean-swept streets. The houses, schools, and churches are painted pink, which complements the green of the tall coconut trees. I remember the most impressive building in this village was the pink cockpit.

The driver informed us it was another fifteen miles to the small barrio where the aged pensionado lived. But on reaching the barrio, we learned that the man lived another two miles over the hill. The car could not travel the narrow road, so we made arrangements to hire a calesa. The calesa driver knew exactly where the man lived, and he would take us there for ten pesos. We left the car and driver in the small barrio. He would wait for our return.

Huddy, Harvel, and I, with the medical kit and my pink parasol, climbed into the back seat of the calesa. It was pouring rain; the driver fastened down the side curtains of the vehicle with pieces of banana leaves. We had gone up the road about a mile when suddenly we came to a halt. The driver said he could go no farther. It seemed he had understood the Doctor perfectly when he had accepted the ten pesos; now he didn't understand a word. We understood though, his calesa could not make it over the hill. The road was very rough, and there were pythons in the area which frightened his little pony. In fact, he told us, a large python could even swallow the dwarfish animal.

At that moment, I was wishing the VIP's back in Washington, who had issued orders to proceed to such an inaccessible place, might be in our place. We were practically lost, darkness was setting in, and a storm was brewing. But orders were orders. The Doctor would carry them out, even if he had to write up his report in the belly of a python.

Soon, out of nowhere, came a little boy riding one carabao and herding another. The driver spoke to him in Visayan and bargained with him to take us over the hill on the carabaos. He, the driver, would wait in the calesa for us to return; it would not take long, for a carabao walked very fast. I was beginning to wonder if we'd be forced to abandon this mode of transportation too, and slither in on the back of an old python.

The Doctor, with his medical kit tucked under his raincoat, road the lead carabao. The little boy, our guide, rode on the animal's rump. Harvel and I mounted the second carabao. She rode up front and carried a banana leaf over her head. I rode on the rear with my pink Chinese parasol stretched in full glory. The old carabao's rump was so broad, I had the feeling I was astride a quonset hut. I was so busy trying to stick on, for the carabao was slick and with not a tuft of hair to hang on to, that I forgot to hold on to my umbrella—the last I saw of it, it was dangling from the limb of a tree.

We arrived at the home of the pensionado. Either we didn't understand our drivers, or they had not understood us, for the man did not live there. He had been living in Cebu City for several years, very near our hotel.

But we did find suffering inside the little nipa hut. Three members of the family were down with malaria. It was a pitiful sight. They shivered on their hard mats, for they had no medicine. The Doctor could give them relief with Atabrine. But he could do little for the aged man who was suffering with a kidney ailment. I shall never forget, when the Doctor knelt beside the mat, how the aged one, wracked in pain, lifted a bony hand and gently stroked the Doctor's cheek. To him "Jesus" had come into the room.

The aged one had no control over his bladder, and to catch the flow of urine, the family had strapped a little bamboo bucket to his leg. The Doctor was able to give him only temporary relief. The grateful family tried to repay us for this mission of mercy with all they had—one ganto of rice.

As we made our way down the hill, I noticed many flickering lights in the nipa huts. I feared there was much suffering all along the way. I was sorry the Doctor could not help them all.

When we arrived back in Cebu City, we went to our room. A mean little typhoon had hit while we were away and had blown out the window panes. A houseboy entered the room with a great armful of banana leaves. "Don't tell me" said the doctor, "that we have to use these things for bedsheets!"

The boy, unmindful of the remark, went over to the window and patched the broken panes with the leaves. As he left the room, the Doctor shook his head. "If anyone says 'banana leaf' to me one more time today ... I'll ..."

We dressed and went down to dinner. The dining room was rather cheerful and the meal was good. We had pancit, lumpia, shrimp, stuffed egg plant, and a delicious salad. We had finished the meal and were waiting for the hot, fresh coconut pie, a favorite dessert in the islands. As the boy removed the salad plates, my husband remarked:

"That salad was the best I've ever eaten. What was it made of?"

"Banana leaves, sir," the boy replied.

The salad was made from the tender, pinkish bud, which is the banana blossom.

Chapter Twelve

WE BOARDED A PLANE for Iloilo City which is on the island of Panay for the last lap of the Doctor's inspection trip. This is the aristocratic city of the archipelago. Before the war, it was the spot where millionaires retired. We were to be the guests of Dr. Carram, former governor of the island, and his charming daughter, Helen. They had a spacious lovely home on the bay, and their hospitality was endless; even a car and a driver were at our disposal. Whenever we returned to Iloilo City, it took on a renewed beauty and interest because of these dear friends.

My particular interest in Iloilo City on this trip was an American, C. N. Hodges, who had in his possession a collection of jewelry estimated to be worth five million pesos; a collection, it was reported, which, if heaped in the center of a room, would reach an eight-foot ceiling. This treasure had been collected over a number of years in a pawn shop which Mr. Hodges owned in Iloilo City.

During the war, the treasure was buried in large cans under an acacia tree by a faithful houseboy. The boy had relied solely on his memory to guide him back to the spot when peace came again to the islands. Had this particular tree been destroyed, likely the jewels might yet be deep in the bosom of the earth. During the war years, Mrs. Hodges was interned for a while at Bacolod, then sent to Santo Tomás in Manila; Hodges and the houseboy took to the hills and were always just one jump ahead of the Japanese. When their shoes wore out, they were replaced with pieces of inner tube tied on their feet. Gunny sacks, wrapped sarong-like, served as clothing. They traveled in circles, the Japs close at their heels but never catching them.

When I inquired in Iloilo City about this King Midas, the people had different opinions. "Oh yes, I know him," said one man. "The old stingy gut. He is so stingy he won't drive his car across the bridge. He walks, or rides a carabao. I remember one time he fell from the animal, face down, in the mud, and the bull walked over him. But old toughie got up, his glasses far down on his nose, and continued on the bull. He always wears green-colored glasses. God knows why. A strange man indeed."

"Sure we know Hodges," said another. "He is worth millions. Yet he will turn out every light in the house, save one. He will keep several electric ice boxes running with nothing in them. The house is always dark and gloomy."

A clergyman said: "Hodges is a good man. He is a Bible student. He has read the Bible through several times. He believes in God and he believes in prayer. But he is not a member of any church."

A doctor said: "He gargles his throat continuously, he is so afraid of germs. Yet his office is as dirty as a pigsty."

A gambler said: "Love of money is his ruling passion. But he doesn't enjoy spending it; he just loves to control it. He leaps from one business to another; he is jack of all trades and master of all. He finds glory in each new business; failure doesn't faze him. He is a trigger-quick in figures, put poor in English and spelling. He is a poor conversationalist. Reads a lot, but it dies within him."

Another said: "He has very little common sense. He wastes more financially than I'd spend in a lifetime. His business is a hodge-podge. He thinks it isn't worth auditing but he loses thousands of dollars because he doesn't."

"Hodges has been in and out of trouble all of his life," said another. "Several times charged with usury, and twice convicted in the lower courts. He loses 80 percent of his court cases because of his great difficulty in expressing himself. Once when sent to jail, he moved his bed and his safe in with him and continued his work through the bars. He had no friends; no money. But he never lost face. I think it embittered him; he lost faith in humanity."

Another man spoke of Hodges as a god. "He has helped more people in Iloilo City than any other living man; many of the big businesses that flourished in the city before the war had their beginnings because of this man. He has always been kind to those needing help."

The next day, we hurried down to No. 77 Guanco Street to see the jeweled king, the old renegade, the old jail bird, the stingy gut, the god of Iloilo wearing green glasses, to see his pile of jewelry that would reach to the ceiling. We came to a two-storied concrete building, shell-pocked, with the windows nailed up with pieces of rusty tin. But over the door was a sign: BANCO de EMPEÑOS.

We entered. The place could have passed for a junk heap, for scattered about were odds and ends of merchandise. Parts of machinery and old greasy tools were heaped on benches and counters. At the rear of the room there was a small cubbyhole partitioned off, for a real estate office. A man, small of stature, sat at a rickety desk that was cluttered with papers. He was wearing green glasses. People were coming and going and he was transacting business at a rapid pace.

C. N. Hodges greeted us very pleasantly. He was a shy man but master of this junk heap. Between the moments he was talking to us, he was carrying on a real estate conference; likely it netted him thousands of pesos. He seemed to treat everyone kindly, and from all appearances they held him in utmost respect, rather than fear. A woman came in and placed seven pesos on the desk. She wanted to redeem a sewing machine. Hodges left the desk to talk with her. "She'll hock it again next week. This makes the twentieth time she has taken it out," he told us.

He took us through a door to a back office to meet his wife, Linnie, a huge woman with an infectious smile. When she learned we had come to see the treasure, she disappeared and soon returned with jewels in dish pans . . . one, two, three, four . . . the pans still came. Mrs. Hodges had no idea of the real value of this collection; she only hoped that in some way they might get it to America, but tax on the collection made it prohibitive. She kept hoping.

I fingered through these jewels: rubies, emeralds, and pearls. I picked up a ring and slipped it on my finger. It was a gorgeous black pearl. This one had grown to twice its size since that long-ago day when it was slipped from some finger and brought to the old pawn shop. And for what? A bowl of rice? Money for medicine for a sick child? Who knows? In that vast treasure of jewels, there went a story with each one; some heartbreaking, others humorous. There was a jeweled comb from the head of a Spanish señorita; a little fan dangling from a long gold chain to tuck at one's belt; bracelets and necklaces.

The diamond collection was not in the dish pans. It was kept in the vault . . . I was amazed that Linnie Hodges knew the price of each item without looking at the tag. This collection had come from every part of the globe. Before the war, when the ships docked, the pawn shops did a rushing business. The tourists, often out of money, headed for Banco de Empeños and left their own jewels for cash, which was spent on island trinkets. Some few returned to redeem the items; others never intended to reclaim them.

C. N. Hodges was a remarkable man; a scholar, but an adventurer. He came by this trait quite naturally. His great-grandmother was a sister of Teddy Roosevelt's mother. He was born in Quinlan, Texas, back in '81, but ran away from home at the age of thirteen after his father had severely horse-whipped him.

He was penniless and hungry. At this very young age, he learned that money was his best friend and was determined to make its acquaintance. He did farm work for mere pennies and room and board. Other jobs paid twenty-five cents a day with room and board. He washed dishes at a hotel and during rest hours hurried out to a cotton field and picked cotton. He worked at a railroad station, pulling the switches and cleaning the station. During his spare time, he learned telegraphy. Despite these hardships, he finished the eighth grade at public school and took a business course at a college in Waco, Texas. Once he banked his meager earnings in his shoe while he hobbled through Texas, and the bills wore out. He appealed to the U.S. Treasury Department and had them replaced.

The army offered him a chance to travel and a salary of fifteen dollars a month. He was only seventeen, but he passed for twenty-one. While in the service, he did the laundry for the other soldiers and boosted his pay to $60 a month and saved every dime of it. He landed in the Philippines in 1898.

Five years later, he took his discharge papers and remained in the islands. He opened a saloon and a dance hall at Camp Jossman for the soldiers. Though he associated with rowdy customers, he remained a teetotaler. He had no time to dance or to gamble. He was out to make money. He had many a Filipina sweetheart, but never married one.

After twelve years in the islands, with poor food, no social life, no sanitation, he returned to the States. After a brief flirtation with Linnie Higdon of Greenville, Texas, he married her. The next day the couple left for Seattle to board the 6,000 ton freighter, *The Tamba Maru*, for Iloilo City. That was many years ago.

Banco de Empeños was first established in 1903 in Guimara at Camp Jossman. It was moved to No. 77 Guanco Street, Iloilo City, after the army moved out of Camp Jossman and shortly after a drunken soldier threw a burning oil sack under Hodges' place and burned him out. Left flat, for he carried no insurance, he had started all over again. He had always been a man who could go from one business to another and find glory in each.

He would scrap and argue over a dollar, even when he had so many he didn't know what to do with them. Shortly after the war, when electric refrigerators in the islands were hard to find, Hodges went to a Chinese man's shop to bargain. The refrigerator was priced forty pesos more than the pawn broker offered. The merchant simply couldn't meet the figure; besides, it was not necessary as there was a demand for this merchandise.

Linnie Hodges wanted the refrigerator but her husband wouldn't budge an inch. She slipped down to the store and laid the extra forty pesos on the counter. "Now you call up my husband and tell him you have decided to meet his price." The sale was completed.

C. N. Hodges had a keen sense of humor: "A pawn broker sees all sides of life without leaving his shop. He hears sad stories and funny ones, without belonging to clubs or going out in society. He is the most despised of God's creatures, yet the most sought after. The rich and the poor come to him when they are in trouble. And yet they are ashamed of the business which brings them to the pawn broker. In reality they should honor it, just as they honor a bank."

All sorts of people and all nationalities visited Hodges. Politicians, society women, poor rice-planting mothers with rough hands and broken fingernails, merchants, artists, reporters, police sergeants, doctors, lawyers, conductors, bankers, out-of-town folk, tourists, priests, sailors, rich and poor, the old and the young— they all came. They came when death entered a home, or when reverses occurred; when the children needed money for school books and clothing; when the bride and groom needed money to furnish a home. At times they seemed to hate the pawn broker because he witnessed their humiliation.

Some folk were so poor, the items they wanted to pawn were

not worth a dime, yet C. N. Hodges always gave them something. One woman came to pawn a worn-out sewing machine for six pesos to bury her child. She cried and begged so hard he gave her the money. She promised faithfully to redeem it the following Monday. That was thirty years before; he still had the sewing machine.

Others deliberately tried to pawn off faked and stolen goods. If the amount was over ten pesos, they were required to have written police clearance with them. That helped prevent theft. Hodges also sent a daily report to the police station, for should he happen to take a stolen article, and a third party should claim it and take the case to court, he would lose.

"The Chinese are very clever in faking things," said the pawn broker. "They dig out the inside of gold and silver money, and fill it with lead. They do wedding rings the same way. We have to test and file each article. The Chinese combine fourteen and four carat gold in watch rims; they even fool me sometimes. Links in chains are done the same way; they use plated links combined with one link of pure gold and one of four carat. I can usually catch them. But the Chinese are good people to deal with; you never have to worry over their loans.

"The Filipinos are quiet and don't fuss about things; they take what I offer them. The British are the worst. Sailors are the most frequent. They usually pawn watches. I don't give them much for I know they won't return. About 60 percent of the people are honest; about 60 percent of the pledges are redeemed.

"Sometimes people try to pass fake money to redeem their goods. Once, a university law student came in to redeem jewelry and tried to pass a fake twenty peso bill. I called the police and turned him over to the authorities, but he went scot free to do it again if he can get by with it.

"A pawnbroker, despised as he may be, has one unfailing source of amusement. If I show up, unexpectedly, at a party, some of the well-known men in Iloilo City turn pale at the gills.

They seem to think I am going to spill the beans. When they see me, they flee for dear life. Several times I have sat alongside men whose dress suits were in my pawn shop, or, perhaps I had loaned them money on a pair of cuff links, or a watch, so they might be able to attend this very function. This man was the whole show, the life of the party; I was the pawn broker. Just common old Shylock.

"I often find myself face to face with society people, men and women, who have surreptitiously visited my shop. They act as if they were afraid I might pull a handful of pawn tickets out of my pocket and wave them before the eyes of the guests. For this reason they fear me and try to ostracize me socially. They simply can't take it if I appear at a party.

"As a matter of fact, I can't begin to remember half of the people who come to me, for around two hundred articles pass over my counter each day. All I know of their lives is what I learn during the few minutes they are in my shop. Not half of them give their right names when they come to pawn goods. The well dressed people are usually Juan da la Cruz, Smith, or Brown.

"It is the bums who pick our distinguished names, such as, Roxas, Ledesma, or Lopez, or even the name of the President of the Philippines. Once a fellow signed his name Manuel Quezon. He came to pawn his fiddle for two dollars. We never ask any questions when they give these high-falutin' names; maybe it is their right name, maybe it isn't. It is none of my business.

"The higher-ups send servants to pawn their jewelry; they are ashamed to come themselves. Once in a great while I get an amusing case. I remember one slick-looking fellow with a pocket full of cigars and wearing a big diamond who gave the name of John Smith. He acted as if he had never been in a pawn shop before. He smiled sheepishly: 'A friend of mine down at the saloon said you might help me out. I am in a hole, only temporarily, of course. I need some money. What will you give me for this diamond ring?'

"It was a good diamond. I named a good sum and he handed it over. He asked me not to put it away too deep, for he would be back in a few days. He did return, not to redeem the ring, but to pawn a diamond pin. A week later, he came in and soaked his cuff links, then his dress suit. He kept coming back, week after week, until he had pawned all of his personal effects. Then he slept on a bench in the plaza. Later, the man found a job, and little by little, he paid back every cent he owed me. He became head of a big business concern here in Iloilo City. But he has high-hatted me since he became prosperous.

"We get a lot of funny things handed to us: false teeth, false eyes, gold crowns from teeth, crowns off the images in churches, church medallions, combs, wooden legs, crutches, pants, Masonic pins, medals from college, class pins, fraternity pins, and rings. Once a man pawned a skeleton he used in a show. He redeemed it and moved on with the show. We never turn down anything in gold and silver. Society folk want quick loans for gambling debts. They'll pawn an item one hour and redeem it the next. Jewelry is the best thing to loan money on; at least 75 percent of my loans are on jewelry. I have specialized in it. I quit taking clothes because moths eat up a dress suit. I had to replace them at a great loss.

"The common things pawned in the islands are sewing machines, wedding rings, key rings, watches, combs, musical instruments, and all kinds of tools. There is no sentiment over a wedding ring. At least 80 percent do not get married; they only live together as man and wife. They quit when they are tired of each other, or start fighting. Soldiers buy these wedding rings for their emergency wives when they are here in the islands.

"Men come in and tell a lie about a death in the family and get money on household things; later an irate wife comes in and contradicts the death-bed story, for the child the husband re-

ported dead is hanging on to her skirts. They are good at playing
on my sympathy. They'll bring in a drove of half-starved, crying
kids, but when I am sure it is a racket, I drive them out of my
shop. Most people believe a pawn broker is a crook. But the pawn
broker business today is operated as a legitimate business.

"We have our regular customers, people who come in each
week with stuff they get a loan on. They couldn't live without a
pawn shop. Some bring in the same bundle on the same day
each week, get the same amount of money on it, and redeem it
the same day. They are honest folk and the loan is only temporary.

"The law demands that we hold pawned goods one year after
the pledges have run out before we sell them. We buy them
back ourselves at the lowest possible figure and keep them until
we can sell them. This is to protect our losses.

"If we should misplace an article and the party who pawned
it finds it out, the article becomes exceedingly valuable. I have
known a 500 peso article to reach 2,000 peso valuation. They
would have a lawyer write us a threatening letter. Should we find
the article among our stock and ask them to redeem it, they
would never take it out. This is a rule among the Filipinos; they
are very slow in paying their interest, but if we put the article
up for sale, they want to kill us. They are great in alleging usury
if your file clerk should make a mistake in figuring the interest."

For over half a century, this old pawn broker had listened to
tales of hardships and woe. And during those years, so his friends
say, he never skinned anyone out of a single dime, if that person tried to do what was right. He made the loan in good faith;
he expected it to be redeemed as such. I took a last glance at
those dishpans full of jewels which could make a pile that
reached the ceiling, and I could understand how he came by
them. It was an honest collection.

As we passed out of Banco de Empeños, I saw an old woman
outside with her sewing machine; a well-dressed man wearing a

flashy diamond; and a sailor fingering a wedding ring, as beside him stood his emergency wife around seven months pregnant. Down the street, we passed the business establishment of the man who once slept in the plaza while his diamonds were hocked in the pawn shop. We passed a Chinese shop and inside a man was drilling the center out of a gold wedding band. C. N. Hodges had touched all of their lives.

On the morrow we headed for Culasi in the province of Antigue on Panay for the last lap of the inspection trip. We had inquired at the local bus station concerning the weather conditions and the possibility of crossing the swollen streams. We could get through by jeep as far as Pangpang, Sibalem River, but we might have to float the jeep over the river by bamboo raft.

The day we set out for Culasi, the typhoon signals were flying in Iloilo City, and the rain was coming down in torrents. We pulled our ponchos tightly around us, put on our helmets, and crawled into a government jeep that was carrying the mail. We sat on mail bags, baskets of smelly dried fish, and government packages.

It was a rugged trip; inch by inch we jogged on. The mail had to go through. The rain came down in solid sheets of water; it was impossible to see two feet ahead of us. Finally the jeep bogged down. We abandoned it, and the driver carried the mail bags to a nearby nipa hut. It was more comfortable than the jeep.

We were only a few miles from our destination, so we hired a calesa to take us the rest of the way. As we started out, the mail carrier entrusted to me a very important package that had just arrived from the States. Would I deliver it to the Alcalde? There was other mail in the bag, and the baskets of fish needed to get through, but this package, it seemed, held priority. And since we were to be the guests of the Alcalde, I agreed to deliver this special package.

Several hours later, our horse-drawn calesa arrived at the barrio. I had lost my helmet and was as drenched as a drowned rat, but still clutched the important parcel. The Alcalde's housekeeper greeted us with the news that he had left that morning for Iloilo City. His house was opened to us. We went inside, hoping to find a dry spot.

Shortly after, the typhoon struck with full fury. When the little mother-of-pearl window panes blew out, the houseboy tried to cover the openings with banana leaves, but it was of little use. The storm reached such intensity that we, along with the Filipinos of the barrio, took refuge in the cockpit, the only substantial shelter. The big circular pit swarmed with people, pigs, and pet fighting cocks, and me, clutching the Alcalde's important package. As the typhoon raged, two men staged a fight between a white and a red rooster to help break the long night.

The morning brought to view a pitiful sight. Nipa huts were flattened like crushed match boxes, but the men were soon at work erecting bamboo poles to be covered with thatched palm leaves. Women with bundles on their heads and babies straddling their hips waded knee-deep in water to help their menfolk.

Since the object of the Doctor's inspection trip, the local hospital, had blown away, we left the next morning for Iloilo City. The housekeeper insisted I take the package to her master who was staying at our own hotel. Our travel by hired jeep was slow and tedious, and when we reached the river, we found the bridge was out. As if by magic, men appeared from all directions carrying bamboo poles which they quickly fashioned into a raft to ferry our jeep across the river.

As I climbed on this native ferry, I was so frightened my foot slipped and I dropped the Alcalde's package into the river. A boy dived in and retrieved it. I hugged the dripping parcel as we were pushed and pulled across the swollen stream by swimming Filipinos, laughing and shouting.

In Iloilo City we were informed that the Alcalde had left for

Manila, and with his new address in my purse, I toted the water-soaked package to our plane. We had almost reached Manila when I discovered the passenger seated next to me was the Alcalde in person. I thrust the package into his hands. "Come hell or high water," the mail had gone through.

His eyes gleamed. Ah, this was the gift he had been waiting for! Quickly he tore off the wrappings. And proudly he held up an autographed picture of President Harry Truman!

You can imagine what condition he was in!

Chapter Thirteen

It was in the month of April, when the cadena de amor was in full bloom, that we buried President Manuel Roxas. I was one of the saddened throng who paid final respects to this great man, the first President of the new Philippine Republic. It was a solemn period; pathos mixed with splendor. I saw many thousands of people with bared heads, slowly moving forward for a last glimpse of their beloved president. Poor rice farmers and their families had traveled long distances and had sat through the night on rainsoaked grasses at Malacañang Palace eating their meager meals of cold fish and rice. Massed columns of soldiers and sailors resplendent in uniforms with shining swords, stood at attention; uniformed attendants at Malacañang Palace opened grates to an endless line of limousines bringing decorated dignitaries from foreign lands; salvos of cannon echoed from the shores and the battleships in the harbor; a canopy of bombers droned overhead.

And thus, in splendor, was buried President Manuel Roxas, on April 25, 1948.

The flowers had not yet withered inside the sealed tomb at North Cemetery, when Huddy and I chanced upon another funeral—that of a poor rice farmer. We were traveling south and were deep in the province when we entered a small barrio. We heard a band playing, and thinking it was a parade, we stopped the jeep to watch it. A woman squatted over a native washtub, ceased the pounding of the clothes, stood up and made the sign of the cross; a barber under a mango tree, cutting a man's hair, paused with scissors in mid-air.

The process drew nearer to the tune of "There'll Be a Hot Time in the Old Town Tonight!" And behind a three-man band, there came six men who carried on bamboo poles a coffin crudely fashioned out of native wood. The bamboo poles were twined with cadena de amor and on the coffin was a basket of rice. José Reyes, the rice farmer, was dead. To many of you, this tune in a funeral procession might appear sacrilegious, but it had been a favorite tune of José's during his lifetime, and his friends wanted to play it for him now that he was gone.

The coffin was borne by men dressed in discarded khaki shorts, but under each waist-band were tucked a few flowers. Behind them, trudged the widow and the children, followed, single file, by about fifty relatives and friends.

The marchers passed out of the barrio, into a coconut grove toward the little church. In silent respect we joined the procession. Farmers, with heads bared, leaned over bamboo gates and made the sign of the cross; naked children ran beside the procession scattering flowers which were crushed under the bare feet of the marchers. There were no bombers droning in the air, but swarms of little rice birds flew overhead.

As we approached the churchyard, the band struck up the tune "The Last Time I Saw Paris" and slowly, oh so slowly, the mourners circled the open grave. The coffin with its basket of rice was lowered.

From the little church came a dozen women, barefooted, wearing native skirts, walking slowly toward the grave, and on each one's head was a bamboo tray filled with blossoms. A weird chant rose from every throat.

As the men covered the coffin, the women tossed in flowers,

mixing orchids with the good earth. As a final tribute they placed at the head of the grave a crude wooden image of Christ. His garment was painted a bright red.

These people, in their simple, beautiful way, had buried José Reyes, the rice farmer.

Chapter Fourteen

WHEN SUMMER COMES to the Philippines, you don't need a calendar because the acacia trees are tattletales. For, at this season, they burst out in full glory with pink blossoms. This tree, sturdy as our southern elm, has a stout trunk like the settled belly of an old man, and its branches spread out like big umbrellas with pink fringes.

It is kind to both man and beast, and often a drama of island life is enacted beneath its shade. The leaves are not large, just small lacy clusters that cling to the branches, strong enough to defy monsoon winds. Yet the pattern of the shadow they cast on the ground resembles the delicate eyelet embroidery made by a young mother sitting in their shade. She used a large hoop, at least four feet in diameter, over which was stretched a piece of pina cloth, and painstakingly embroidered a design while a naked baby nursed at her breast. An aged woman, resting under the shade of the acacia tree, bent over a little clay stove cooking a pot of rice. Little boys climbed the trees to break off dead twigs to fire the stove. A carretela halted in its shade to let the dwarfish pony munch green grasses that grew in a nearby corner.

An aged man lingered by the side of the tiled archway of the ruins of a palatial home. He moved over to the friendly shade of an acacia tree and removed his hat. He stood very still. Was he praying? Or, was he recalling happy days spent in this spacious courtyard with friends now dead, victims of a Jap bomb? Who knows? The old man passed on down the street, crossed over to Malata Church and entered.

I was on my way to attend a Red Cross Tea at Malacanang Palace. I had not been inside the Palace since the death of Manuel Roxas. I was hoping I might get a peep at the 5,000 peso bed in which President Quirino slept, according to newspaper reports. He had been in for a lot of criticism over this old bed with its massively carved headboard. Likely, the bed wasn't worth over a couple of hundred pesos; nevertheless, it had gotten adverse publicity.

The tea was a sumptuous affair that cost, no doubt, thousands of pesos. The food was elaborately displayed; dozens and dozens of extra servants were hired; hot-house flowers decorated the rooms; and from the chandeliers burned a thousand candles. The women came in their best ternos fashioned of beautiful pina cloth, or gorgeously sequined material; they wore elaborate hair-dos, beaded zapatillas, and orchid corsages. The women of the Philippines have a custom: one should never be seen in the same dress twice. Each woman vies with the other to win the title of being the best dressed. And at this tea I, in my plain pink linen dress, felt like a country cousin.

The beautifully gowned women milled about the Palace flourishing expensive Spanish fans as they sipped iced papaya juice or calamansi juice. I kept wishing they would wander over to the edge of the spacious terrace and look out across the Pasig River, for there, almost within a stone's throw, were the hovels of the poor who lived like pigs in wallows. These destitute people existed on the bank of the Pasig under pieces of tarpaulin discarded by the army.

Even the stench of this area wafted across the water and mingled with the fragrance of the sampaguita. Had the voices on the terrace been hushed for a moment, one could hear the cries of sick and hungry children. I walked to the far edge of the terrace and watched a woman, so thin that her arms and hands resembled bird claws, carrying hot, muddy water from the river to bathe the brow of a child on a dirty mat. It seemed I could hear the fretful voice, begging for a drink of cold water. Could he hear the tinkling of ice in the glasses at our tea table? I turned, sick at heart, as I wandered back to the crowd.

I stood near two women who were discussing the Red Cross Drive. One remarked that she could contribute only ten pesos because she had spent over three hundred on the gown that she wore. I glanced at the group of women and quickly figured in my mind the amount they had spent on the new clothes for this elaborate affair. I tried to estimate the cost of the dainties on the tea table—enough to buy a year's supply of rice for one poor family across the Pasig.

I could not sip the iced papaya juice, for I seemed to hear the cry of the sick child across the river. Quietly, I made my way out of the palace and hurried on to Quiapo Market and down Echague Street. I walked under the viaduct and on to banks of the Pasig. I must find the little boy was was crying for the cool drink. I paused on the little bridge that spans the river, and the sight I beheld would turn a strong man sick in the pit of his stomach: dozens and dozens of families living in unbelievable squalor, under the shelter of greasy, black tarpaulins. On the banks of the Pasig there was no acacia tree to offer a friendly shade; a merciless sun beat down on the makeshift shelters and the greasy tarpaulin roofs sizzled and smoked.

Then I spotted the shelter where the little boy lay upon a mat. This make-shift home was scarcely six feet by six and stood on the very banks of the Pasig River amidst dirt and grime washed ashore. Approaching was a woman with a few scant provisions in her basket: a small head of cabbage, a few long Bombay beans, a dried fish, and a handful of rice. Just outside the shelter sat a woman at a Filipino wash tub, her legs so thin they resembled young bamboo shoots.

As I stood gazing at this scene of abject poverty, a skinny little girl, perhaps five years old, came skipping toward me. Despite the depressing surroundings her eyes were bright as stars; she appeared gay and happy. She was clad in an adult's blouse of pale blue silk. The sleeves dangled far below her small hands and she kept pushing them up; the hem of the blouse touched her ankles.

"Hello," I called out, and she came running toward me. "Do you live there?" I indicated the shelter.

"Yes," she answered, then danced away.

Tears came into my eyes. Even the animals in the forest had better shelter. Where was the Red Cross, that such sordid living should exist? Then I remembered—it was just across the river. I could still hear the music from the Palace.

I wanted to cry out for help. Would someone help these poor people? My heart told me that all people who were hungry and sick were my charges. I could not buy them a new home, nor could I support them, but I could cry out their need for help, their need for a decent living.

I watched the woman offer the fretful boy a cup of water, too hot to relieve his feverished lips. I called to the little girl. She danced back to me. I reached into my purse for the ten pesos that I should have left on the tea table; I added to it another ten pesos, all the money I had with me. I pressed it into the child's hand and told her to take it to the woman bending over the sick child. "Thank you, good Americana" she said in perfect English. She ran with all her might toward the shelter, gathering up the hem of the long blouse so she would not stumble.

"The Americana! The Americana!" I heard her call out, as she thrust the money into the woman's hand. The old woman made the sign of the cross, first, then lifted her hand to thank me. I watched the little girl dash away to an ice cream vendor and return with an ice cream cone for the thirsty little boy.

Across the Pasig, the president's palatial yacht was anchored. Could he not see this poverty when he boarded the yacht to take a run down the river? Upstairs, I remembered, was that massive five thousand peso bed. And in that moment my fancy ran wild. If I could sell the president's bed—oh! if I could! How I would like to wipe out, forever, this sordid scene. If I just had the five thousand pesos, I could build a little nipa shack down Tagaytay Road where the white bud trees bloomed and little rice birds fluttered over rice stacks, and there would be an old carabao for the little boy to ride. There would be bananas, papayas, mangos, fish, and rice, and clean washing fluttering from the clothesline. Here would be the sweet smell of the good earth.

After I had settled this family so well in the country, I thought of a better plan. Why not *auction* off the president's bed? There were wealthy Filipinos who would pay a handsome sum for this bed. And, again in my wild fancy, I put the bed up for auction. Going. Going. Gone. Sold for fifty thousand pesos. In five minutes time I had spent the entire amount for I had provided a good home for every family living in squalor on the banks of the Pasig.

While I was busy settling my charges in their little nipa huts, I had forgotten—where would the president sleep? Oh, I'd make some arrangements. Soon I had the little boy's father dressed in a beautiful barong-Tagalog made of embroidered pina cloth and his black trousers had a satin stripe down the sides. The president had been dressed in this fashion when I had left the palace. Likely my charge, the old man, had never owned a fancy barong Tagalog. Why not let *him* wear it? After all, I had the president sleeping on a mat on the floor at this stage.

Suddenly, I was brought back to earth. Someone was tapping me on the shoulder. Oh dear! the police were after me. I remembered that the fifty thousand peso bed didn't belong to me. I had no right to sell it. I turned quickly and faced a vendor. "You buy my orchids, Mom?" he said.

It was such a pity to come back to earth and to the scene on the Pasig. The poor father was still wearing an old gunny sack wrapped diaper-wise around him; the old woman was still swishing a banana leaf to shoo the flies from the little boy's face; the little girl in the long blouse was playing hop-skip on the greasy banks of the river, as she ate an ice cream cone.

If Ramón Magsaysay had been president, there would have been someone to whom I could cry for help. I could have called up Malacañang Palace and told him about the plight of the poor Filipino family. I could hear him saying: "Send them up to the palace and we'll bed them down for the night." Then, like as not, he'd have boomed out: "By the way, do you need a pair of my britches for the old man?"

It is a comforting thought to know that since his presidency, these sordid barong-barongs no longer exist on the banks of the Pasig.

Chapter Fifteen

PERHAPS THE HIGH POINT of my newspaper career in the Philippines was my being invited by Juan Orendain, head of Malacañang Press, to attend the Economic Conference of Asia and the Far East, known as ECAFE, or the little United Nations. The meeting was held at the palatial Mansion House in Baguio, the summer capitol of the Philippines.

Juan had a chair for me in the spacious press gallery and I was billeted at the Baguio Country Club at the expense of the Philippine Government. I felt inadequate, for billeted at this club were the newspaper brains of the world. And what was I doing there? No doubt, these high-powered newsmen asked the same question. Actually, my assignment was sort of a good will tour; I was to mix and mingle with the delegates and write human interest stories. The kind the "big boys" ignore.

My chair in the press gallery was next to Mr. Yaxshainz, Tass News Agency for the U.S.S.R. I made a special effort to be nice to this Russian.

It seemed every five minutes Mr. Yaxshainz jumped up and rushed out of the press room, no doubt to wire Moscow every time the Russian delegation voted. Their vote was invariably "No!" Each time he left and returned, he stepped on my toes and swished his coat tail in my face. Even though my toes were bruised and my nose raw from the numerous tweedy slaps of his coat tail, I always smiled sweetly when he returned and flopped his bulk into his seat, hogging the arm of my chair in addition to his own.

My job wasn't easy. How on earth could I get a human interest story from the bearded delegate from Pakistan, who supposedly could speak not one word of English. I admired his flowing bloomers made of white satin, his velvet bolero, and his turban. I even tried to estimate the yardage in the folds of his head gear, which was fashioned as deftly as a John Frederick. All I could do was to write a little story about the way he was dressed. Either he *could* read English or some had translated the item to him, for the next day, he came to me and bowed his thanks so deeply, I was sure his turban would drop at my feet.

The Siamese delegation and I found common ground. We talked about Siamese cats. I learned that this sacred animal, even though it never inherited a baseball team, was ten times smarter than Rhubarb. Each home in Thailand must have a cat, just as our homes must have a Bible.

At mealtime each delegation was served at its own table in a large dining hall. The way to get human interest stories was to do "table hopping." I decided that I would dine with a different delegation each day. First, I would dine with Mr. Stetsenko and his Russian delegation, for there was a vacant chair at the large table. Mr. Stetsenko evidently decided differently, for as I approached, he reached over and tilted the back of the chair against the table. That was drawing the iron curtain, if you please. However, I ignored his rudeness, paused, and chatted with him very cheerfully for a few minutes before passing on.

At the table of the Ceylon delegation, I dined with Mr. Amarasooriya who taught me to spread butter on a banana and eat it for bread with pork. The sad-eyed, gaunt men from Ceylon ate sparingly and always spoke of the hunger of their people. Yet, Mr. Amarasooriya wore a diamond as big as a button on his vest. I wondered why he had journeyed so many miles to plead for another cup of rice for his people. Why not sell the diamond?

Miss Dju-bu-yao—she was the "Eleanor Roosevelt" from China—graciously invited me to sit at her table. She handed me a pair of chop sticks and tried to teach me to use them. When she had long finished her bowl of rice, I was still chasing a grain over the table, trying to get it in the clutches of my chop sticks so I might convey it to my mouth. Miss Dju-bu-yao waved aside a platter of meat and reminded me that people in China were starving; we must eat sparingly. I glanced at her Chinese dress, fashioned of expensive silk brocade. She must have read my mind, for she said: "I wear this silk for it helps my people. It helps the ones who raise the silkworms and the ones who weave. If I did not buy, they could not work."

My friends from Nationalist China reminded me of our own Indians; their phonetic language and their names bear a resemblance.

Another member of the Chinese delegation was pretty Irene Cheng, whose real name was Yen-Sen, which means "I was born in Peking." Her son was Bee-Lein, a name which means "on the level."

At the table of the Indian delegation, I dined with Mr. Saksena from Bombay. Since I failed at noon to get the rice grain on my chop sticks, I was downright hungry by evening. We had curried chicken, and the way they hack up a fowl, the portions were mere bits. So, when the platter was passed, I took a second helping. Mr. Saksena was astonished. "You Americans eat too much." Then he reminded me of India's hunger, and I simply couldn't touch any more food.

Having become acquainted with these delegates from the Far East, I, also, soon became gaunt and hungry as ECAFE dragged on.

True, my friends practiced what they preached: to eat sparingly. Yet, for this conference, thousands of lights burned in the Mansion Hall just for show. Had they been turned off, the money saved would have bought much rice; outside stood expen-

sive cars bought by the government to transport these delegates
(and the press, including me) to and from the Mansion House although a bus ran every fifteen minutes. Millions of dollars had
been spent trying to decide if the starving people could have another bowl of rice, yet when the decision was reached, I
wondered how much money was left to buy food for the starving
people.

And did I make friends with Russia? I had written a very
fine article on this subject for my paper, but had not sent it in.
Then, one day I locked horns with Mr. Yaxshainz. I happened
to mention the American school in Shanghai (this was before
the city fell to Communist China) which had been organized
under the auspices of the University of Chicago, just as had the
American School in Manila. When I mentioned this school, the
Russian blurted out: "Damn the American School! Damn the
ones that run it!" I kept very quiet and didn't mention that I
was head of Journalism in the American School in Manila. It
seemed that Mr. Yaxshainz's daughter and several other Russian
pupils had been dismissed from the Shanghai School.

I didn't know the details concerning the incident, nor did I
ask. But I did know the American School in Shanghai flew the
American flag, and right or wrong it was my flag. He might
swish his coat tail in my face, but he dared not swish it in my
country's face. A few minutes later, up jumped the Tass News
Agency reporter to wire Moscow; the Russian delegation had just
bellowed another "NO." By this time I had lost my patience so
when he returned to take his chair beside me, I yanked his coat
tail out of my face and said very curtly: "Mr. Yaxshainz, do
Russians know how to say, pardon me, please?"

There was another high point in my newspaper career. I was
made a member of the Manila Overseas Press Club, and I believe I was the first woman to be admitted to the exclusive club.
When I applied for membership I was told this Club was a man's

world off limits to females. However the Club issued me a Guest Card and later admitted me as a full-fledged member. I am sure today the Manila Overseas Press Club has many women who are members for the newspaper women in Manila are excellent reporters.

Chapter Sixteen

๛ THE GODS OF THE ISLANDS were angered; and in a moment of revenge, all hell broke loose. Iloilo City was rocked with an earthquake. The earth tumbled, groaned, shook, then ripped wide open with crevices so deep that cars, jeeps, and carabaos dropped out of sight. The old churches that had withstood centuries of floods, typhoons, and wars tumbled to the ground like toy blocks. Night after night the earth rumbled; the tremors were felt as far north as Manila. Night after night in the little quonset hut, our beds were rocked like cradles by the angry gods.

Josie picked up her prayer book and hurried on to mass. The girl across the street, Ramona, too frightened to carry on with her work, hurried up to Quiapo Market and bought three twisted roots from an old vendor; these she placed under her pillow to keep away the evil spirits. José stood on the sea wall and scanned land, sea, and sky for a sign. And he found one . . . a dark cloud rising up in the sky over toward Legaspi.

"It's the volcano, Mom," he said. "It is Mt. Mayon. It may bury us alive!"

I reminded him that Mt. Mayon was sixty-five miles away.

"But Mom, once it was angry and it spit ashes all the way to Manila!" A few minutes later, when he came up to coconut the floors, he was wearing his rosary around his neck. He was quiet and apprehensive.

José was right. The evening paper told the story. Mt. Mayon was erupting with a fury that might equal the disastrous eruption that occurred on February 1, 1814. On that day, a stream of lava and ashes buried the whole countryside around the barrios of Budiao, Camalig, almost destroyed Guinabatan and Abay, and completely destroyed the town of Kagsawa, killing over 1200 people. The winds carried the showers of volcanic ash as far as the coast of China, and ash-laden clouds, turning day into night, covered Northern Luzon as well as Panay.

José listened intently to the news, then asked if he might have an hour off to go to Malate Church. He started out, but soon returned for an advance of one peso to buy candles to light. I gave him two pesos.

Mt. Mayon's eruption continued for days. It had seen generations strut and fret their little hour, for against its background men had spent their lives in petty follies and in inglorious toil. The people of the Philippines worshipped this mountain. They would stand before it in awe, wonder, and fear, something akin to the feeling of the supernatural. It cast its spell upon those who dwelt within its shadow; even school children in the nearby towns sang the first line of the National Anthem with these words: "I love Mayon! My native land!"

Mt. Mayon, with an elevation of 7, 941 feet, is the most perfect volcanic cone in the world. As one approaches this sleeping beauty, it appears silhouetted like an inverted fan against the sky. On clear days, its image is reflected perfectly in the lake below. It has known peaceful days; sleepy, golden ones. A small village of thatched-roofed houses drowses at its feet in the intense sunlight; bull carts amble along the road loaded with long stalks of golden bamboo; and little children play within its shadows.

Now it writhed in a swirling mass of black clouds that boiled toward the sky like a huge funnel. It belched molten lava and spat out hot rocks and ashes. It was a drunken sloth. There began the exodus of the inhabitants, but when it ceased spewing lava, they would return to dig in the ashes. They had done this for centuries.

One of the earliest eruptions was recorded in 1616, but no account was given of the destruction. In June, 1766, it erupted again and continued for six days. In October, the heavy rains dislodged the sheets of disintegrated ejecta from the slopes and whole villages and plantations were buried.

During its years of silence, men would risk their lives to scale its majestic peaks, to try to find out what made it subject to such violent fits of passion. In 1592, two Fransican padres almost succeeded in gaining the summit; in May, 1823, Captain D. Antonio Liguienza did reach the summit and made a report to a Spanish scientific society; later, two Scotchmen attempted to duplicate the captain's feat. Two writers, Jagor in 1856, and von Drasche in 1876, shared honors in attaining the summit and gave to the world a full description of the Mt. Mayon crater.

Neither Josie's prayers, José's candle-lighting, nor Ramona's twisted roots under the pillow, seemed to appease the angry gods. The spiteful volcano continued to erupt.

Then the rains came. There was quite a downpour in the afternoon, but by dark it was just a patter on the tin roof of the quonset. I knew the gods were angry, for JoJo was my best barometer. If a storm was coming, the cat sensed it. That night, he yowled like a panther, crawled under the sheets, and slept at our feet. After he quieted, we dropped off to sleep. At three o'clock I roused, for he was sitting on my pillow with his head thrown back, yowling loudly. I arose to check on the weather. During flashes of lightning, I could see the entire embassy compound was under water; the quonset huts resembled a Moro village on its stilts. I watched a dish pan, buckets, baskets, door steps, everything that could float, heading toward the sea wall.

I rushed downstairs. The girls were sleeping on army hospital beds, but I feared the water had already reached the mattresses. Half-way down the steps, the water was lashing my ankles. I called to Josie. The water was level with the mattress on her bed; in another five minutes, it would have covered her face.

We brought them upstairs and sat down to wait until daylight. There was no wind; just a steady rain. We heard our neighbors up and down the street of the compound try to start cars. It was of no use; the motors were flooded. They waded water hip-deep back to their quonsets.

Manila went under water. All schools and all government offices were closed. Business took a holiday. Sewers were clogged, and the outlets through the sea wall were stopped up. Policemen waded water chest-high to prevent pilfering; an amphibious army duck hauled a few passengers to and from Manila Hotel. Little boys and girls went floating down the boulevard on rafts made of banana leaves. The puto vendor climbed in the fork of an acacia tree and carried on business, asking four times the regular price for the small rice cakes. People came in bancas to buy his wares.

The typhoons lashed far to the north, destroying the rice crops. At Cabanatuan, near the infamous prison, where our American boys had been interned, an army of worms invaded the farms and left vast areas denuded. Governor Juan O. Chico, in sending out a distress call, mobilized the children in the province of Nueva Ecija against this onslaught of worms that soon might lay waste the rice fields and make empty the granaries. The children gathered such great heaps of worms that the governor requested the men to look about for a certain old magician who could lead the pests to their doom, as if he were the Pied Piper of Hamlin.

The magician, an old farmer of the barrio Mayapyap, reportedly could destroy worms by merely uttering weird incantations and spitting on the infested area. How one old man could produce enough spittle for the thousands of acres was not explained. The story merely said that after the mumbling and spitting ceremonies the army of worms would follow the old man and would squirm with joy at the privilege of being destroyed.

While havoc swept over the islands, there came to pass a wave of "miracles." The most spectacular was "The Shower of Rose Petals," at Lipa. This "miracle," or "manifestation," continued over many weeks and drew crowds of tens of thousands every day. People came from foreign lands and the fame of the rose petal cure even reached the United States.

The angry gods were forgotten. The shower of rose petals became the subject of conversation at all bridge parties and was used as a topic for sermons in pulpits. The petals, reputedly, brought about cures for many ills, restored the dead to life, and brought new hope to the islands and its people.

"The Shower of Rose Petals" happened within the cloister and on the grounds of the Carmel Convent at Lipa City, sixty-three miles south of Manila. The fifteen sisters in the convent had led a quiet, sheltered life, out of touch with the world—except through their parents, brothers, and sisters—until one calm September day when the rose petals fell. Then the world moved in on them.

Sister Terecita Castillo, a Carmelite postulate, was walking in the garden around five o'clock on the afternoon of September 13, 1948. She observed a vine shaking vigorously as if whipped by a strong gale, yet there was no wind, and no other leaves in the garden stirred. When she approached the vine, she heard a gentle voice: "Fear not, my child. Whatever I shall tell you to do, you must do. For fifteen consecutive days come to visit me here at this spot." Sister Terecita raised the branches of the vine and looked in vain. She could see no one.

The next day, she went again and knelt by the vine to recite a "Hail Mary." When she was reciting the words, "full of grace," the vine moved and she beheld Our Lady who appeared with her hands clasped on her breasts with a golden rosary in her right hand. She was dressed in pure white and her bare feet rested on a cloud scarcely three feet from the ground.

On Tuesday, at the same hour, the little sister again beheld

Our Lady with her arms extended as if she would embrace her. "I wish this spot to be blessed tomorrow," the voice said.

The next day, at the hour of three, Bishop Alfredo Ma. Obviar, chaplain to the Carmelites, wearing the rochette and stole, led the community to the spot and blessed the nook. Only little Sister Terecita saw the vision of Our Lady and only she heard these words: "Gather the petals." But when the apparition vanished, the ground was strewn with rose petals.

And yet only the little sister saw the rose petals. When she told the story, the Mother Superior discounted it. The young girl started to cry. Instead of tears, there were drops of blood rolling down her cheek. She could no longer see. Then a strange thing happened . . . the Mother Superior smelled the fragrance of rose petals, yet she knew no roses grew in the garden. Then she, too, saw the rose petals. She arose and kissed the eyelids of the little sister, and once again she could see.

Again and again Our Lady and the little sister met at the vine. One day the apparition asked from the community individual consecration of its members to Her according to Her spirit of St. Grignon de Montfort.

Then the shower of rose petals started. On September 30, rose petals were strewn in the cells of the convent. On October 3, a shower of rose petals fell on the stairway and within the cloister. It was on November 11 that they fell outside the convent for the first time.

On November 12, Sister Terecita visited the nook; and there, against the vine, was Mary, Mediatrix of All Grace, with her hands clasped on her breast in an attitude of prayer. She looked tenderly but sadly on the young nun, and spoke her farewell words: "When people come to pray and ask for grace, let them ask directly to Me. These things may now be revealed. This is my last apparition on this spot."

And these things were revealed. The daily papers in Manila headlined this story: "The Miracle of the Rose Petals at Lipa."

There were other big stories in the news: the Huks had raided a barrio in Tarlac and had beheaded twelve farmers; Chiang Kai-shek had flown from Formosa and had dined with President Quirino to discuss world events; evacuees were pouring in from fallen Shanghai. All were big stories, but they went below the fold; the story of the rose petals was headlined. The fame of this "miracle" not only spread through the length and the breadth of the islands, it took on an international interest. The Philippine Air Force received inquiries from the United States, and from tourists on the European continent, asking if the Fernando Air Base near Lipa could accommodate giant airplanes.

Each day the people flocked by the thousands to witness the shower of petals. They came from every walk of life: the rich, the poor, the believers, the scoffers, members of congress, the President of the Philippines, the members of the Women's International League, bus loads of university students from every part of the islands. The small city of Lipa overnight became a mecca. It was reported that on one Sunday, 30,000 people flocked to the Carmel Convent. Should a morning paper run a headline: "Heavy Petal Showers Fall Anew at Lipa," the people would rush toward the site. Often the traffic was four cars deep. All were hoping to witness the shower of rose petals.

I read the papers concerning the rose petal showers with great interest, and always read them aloud to José. Huddy argued the whole thing was a hoax, and Harvel agreed. But José was a believer: "Sir, the rose petals do fall."

Julie kept quiet, but Josie spoke up: "Don't truth the story, Mom!" She had an idea that one of the sisters at the Carmel Convent was gathering rose petals during the dark hours and would blow them through a big bellows at certain hours each day, or, whenever she wanted to have a rose petal shower.

Josie remembered an incident of her childhood when a similar "miracle" proved to be a hoax. In the old church in Laoog there was the statue of a saint that wept real tears during the Lenten season. Each day, Josie and her grandmother trudged many miles to kneel before this statue to pray, and to leave an offering. One day, while the aged grandmother was praying earnestly, little Josie slipped behind the altar; it was a childish desire to peek. She saw the priest behind the curtain. In his hand, he held a small bulb that was attached to a long rubber tube. This connected with the eye sockets of the statue of the saint. He pumped the water—slowly, oh so slowly, and the blessed saint's tears dropped one by one.

Josie could hardly wait until they were out of the church so she could tell her grandmother. Now, they would not have to walk this long distance to church; nor would they have to drop their hard-earned money in the box. Grandmother didn't wait until they reached home to punish Josie. Right under the big mango tree she made the child stretch out her hands. She lashed the palms of Josie's hands again and again with a small wooden paddle. She lashed them until they bled.

When I asked Huddy if José and I might drive to Lipa on Sunday, he was astonished. Would I be so foolish as to brave that throng at Lipa? I would.

When Sunday arrived, the entire family wanted to go along. "Adam" was loaded to the hilt. Huddy and I rode up front; Harvel, Josie, and Julie, in the back seat, with José at their feet on the floor board. Off we went!

At Lipa, the traffic was six cars deep. We waited in line for an hour, then moved up inch by inch. During the wait, Harvel, Josie, and Julie gathered ferns from the roadside to plant in our garden. José and I scanned the sky for a sign of falling petals. Huddy remained in "Adam," for beggars swarmed around the car and reached out their hands for money. They had taken advantage of the situation and the frame of mind of the people. Huddy gave them coins and I watched them withdraw to the shade of a tree to count their money.

The Carmel Convent stood on a little rise and was framed

with coconut trees. The new building was of gray concrete, and the white cross stood out against the gray clouds. Women with parasols of many colors pushed among the seething mob. High above the crowd rose a cluster of gay-colored balloons. Men, women, and little boys were selling horse-racing tickets to the people who were waiting in line to enter the church. An old woman pushed her way through the crowd yelling: "Baluts!" The noise and the voices of the vendors drowned out the solemn voice of the priest who was saying a mass transmitted by a loud-speaker to the waiting crowd.

We arrived at the convent shortly after noon, only to be informed that a heavy shower of petals had fallen at ten o'clock that morning. This shower had caused a near-panic among the pilgrims who had tried to pick up petals. Huddy didn't believe a word of it; he was sure the rose petals from a nearby garden had been caught up by a whirlwind and showered over the convent roof. Just a freak of nature.

One man to whom I spoke had witnessed the shower, and said it was quite extraordinary. The petals had dropped out of no-where, spilling like a great spray of pink water on the roof of the convent.

A boy, Guillermo Milan of Lipa, had been a scoffer, but when he saw the petals fall on the roof, he rushed over and scaled the convent wall. According to his own story, he felt as though he were walking on air, and he went straight to the corner of the roof where the petals had fallen, as if he were directed by some mysterious power. He collected thirty rose petals.

There was a woman in the group who had brought along a tightly-corked bottle into which she would place the petals should they fall, and should she be lucky enough to grab some. She had been so jostled by the crowd that she could not get near the petals. Then another "miracle" happened. When she looked at her bottle there was a rose petal inside!

José listened intently to these stories, then quietly walked away. He was gone for a while, then returned to me and whispered: "Mom, I have one! I have a petal!" He pulled me aside and opened his clenched fist. In the palm of his hand was a pink rose petal. At the edge of the crowd, he had seen it drifting in the air; he had chased and grabbed it as he would a butterfly. He was trembling with excitement: "Mom, I must get home with it so I cure my grandmother. Her bones ache all the time."

I knew I must believe José's story, for he believed it. He did hold a rose petal in the palm of his hand. I gave him a piece of Kleenex in which to wrap the petal; he placed it in his shirt pocket and buttoned down the flap.

"José, we won't tell anyone about your good luck. Let's keep it a secret!" He agreed. I simply could not have the family chide him. For *he* believed.

As we drove home, the conversation concerned the shower of rose petals. The family was convinced more than ever it was a hoax. José and I remained silent, occasionally exchanging knowing glances.

It was reported that one of the heaviest showers of rose petals had fallen the day that Judge and Mrs. Modesto Castillo, parents of little Sister Terecita, had visited the Carmel Convent. Terecita, who had been kept inside the convent, came out to visit with her parents. After they had witnessed this heavy shower of petals, the parents, deeply touched, had asked Terecita what she desired most for a gift. She replied humbly: "A doll."

So the stories went. People throughout the islands offered as high as one hundred pesos for a single petal. The priests and the nuns became alarmed at this madness; they sent out a warning that no rose petal from Lipa could be sold at any time. None were for sale. The rose petal vendors who preyed upon the people were quickly defeated.

There was a wave of cures for many maladies. Incurable

diseases were reported to be cured simply by applying a rose petal from Lipa to the affected parts. The doctors in Manila and Batangas, including men of high standing—Dr. Pantin, Dr. Katigbak, and Dr. Roxas—testified they had seen these "miracles" happen. Two instances of deafness were reported cured. Back in Baltimore a young American girl who was dying in Mercy Hospital with pneumonia was saved by a rose petal from Lipa, so the story went. A Filipino priest, studying at the University of Baltimore, had been the recipient of a rose petal sent to him by his sister who was a nun at the Carmel Convent. When there appeared no other remedy to save the girl's life, the priest offered to use the petal. When it was applied to her body, the fever dropped immediately.

At Dumanjug near Cebu City, the ninety-seven-year-old Juan Alpuerto was dead. The members of the family were crying around Juan's bed. Suddenly, Rose Alpuerto remembered a bottle of water she had brought from Lipa when she had gone to see the rose petal shower. Quickly, she grabbed the bottle of water and poured the contents, drop by drop, down the dead man's throat. He opened his eyes and sat up in bed. An hour later, he was eating a bowl of rice.

José had carried his rose petal to Pasay and his grandmother had bound it to her swollen knees. By morning, the pain was gone and she was able to walk again. The family had taken the rose petal to Angeles so an uncle might be cured of his rheumatism. That was the last I heard of José's rose petal. He still believed in this miracle, and the wonderment that the petal should have drifted his way.

But I did witness a rose petal cure. My good friend, Betty Ronquillo, president of the International Women's League and a very brilliant woman, had journeyed to Lipa and had knelt to pray before the image of Our Lady Mediatrix of Grace. While Betty prayed, a sister placed in her hand a rose petal. It was a few days later that the League was scheduled to hold a tea at

Malacañang Palace to honor Daddy (Irving) Hart who had been in the Philippines over half a century doing educational work among the Filipinos. Daddy Hart started his welfare work in 1906 when he became interested in the Culion Leper Colony.

The day before we were to hold the tea, Betty fell down the stairs and twisted her ankle. I went over to see her. The ankle was swollen three times its normal size and Betty was in such pain she could not put her weight upon her left foot. I was very certain that she would arrive at the tea on crutches, for knowing Betty I knew she would be there to attend to her duties.

The next day we gathered for the tea. The honored guest was on the platform. Betty arrived wearing a beautiful gold-colored terno. She walked to the rostrum without the slightest limp. I glanced at her ankle: it was no longer swollen.

After the program, I asked what had happened. Betty replied: "Last night when I was in such pain, I happened to remember my rose petal. I bound it to my ankle. The pain left; the swelling and the soreness are gone."

A few days later I met my good Indian friend, Mrs. Jagtiana, who was trying to hail a taxi to rush out to the hospital where her mother lay seriously ill. In her hand, she clutched a folded piece of paper which contained a rose petal. She had borrowed it from Betty Ronquillo. She was hurrying out to the hospital to bind it to her mother's head.

Up and down the islands, "miracles" were reported. A heavy shower of rose petals, each petal bearing the image of Christ and the Virgin Mary, was seen in San Rafael, Bulacan. The petals fell on the sidewalk in front of Dr. Arcadio de Castro's home. Up at Laoog, in Ilocos Norte, the people were flocking to the Dingras Aglipayan Church, where it was reported an illuminated image of Christ bearing the Cross was projected on the church door which was made of old galvanized iron. In the small village of Palaka of Miahao Town near Iloilo City, the eleven-year-old Hermina Mondido beheld the Virgin Mary and Infant Son Jesus under a mango tree. They were surrounded by brilliant halos. After she beheld the image, a beautiful religious medal dropped at her feet. It was the size of a fifty-centavo piece, and on it was the image of Christ. At Davao, an illiterate Cebuano faith healer and tuba (native wine) addict had a bleeding image of St. Vicente Ferrer which he exhibited in the Piapi slum district of that city. Blood, or what appeared to be blood, exuding sweet scents, flowed from the left hand, elbows, and feet of the image. The old tuba addict said he bought the image from a transient peddler. At Porac, Pampanga, the crowd flocked to see the image of Our Lady Mediatrix appear on a tamarind tree. A little crippled girl, twelve-year-old Estalita Pinada, wandered near the tree and saw a halo of light. When the little girl kissed the Holy Rosary she held in her hand, she was immediately cured of her lameness.

The miracle of the rose petals of Lipa had brought good to the islands. Let the scoffers say a nun was hidden behind a wall pumping the petals into the air. This beauty of the rose petals filled a need in the minds of the Filipinos. They had just endured a long and brutal war. In times of stress, such as these, they felt a strong urge for something greater than their puny selves. It is small wonder that people will turn to religion, to "miracles," even to superstitions and soothsaying? They need something to cling to that will give them a feeling of security in an insecure and troubled world.

The shower of rose petals came at a time when the communist Hukbalababs were a scourge to the island of Luzon. Each day brought news of death and destruction left in their path. There was no place in the Huk stronghold considered safe for man or beast. And yet, from the very heart of Huk land, people emerged by the thousands and made their way to Lipa to witness the Shower of Rose Petals. There was not one single instance ever recorded that anyone making a pilgrimage to Lipa was murdered by the Huks.

About this time, Josie's father, blind and crippled with rheumatism, came from Ilocos Norte to visit her. The father had learned of another "miracle" at Agoo, La Union. There, a fifteen-year-old boy named José Fargon had a miraculous well near his house, the waters of which had curative powers. The Benguet Igorots who were flocking to the well, claimed the boy had the curative powers of an "Apo Iro," a native healer. The young healer, son of a poor rice farmer, was in the fifth grade at school. He attended classes, then cared for his patients after hours. He would accept no pay, but many left gifts of ducks, chickens and gantos of rice.

Josie's father had learned some of the background of this story from an Igorot: the boy had had a dream one night. A voice bade him dig a well at the south corner of the nipa hut. The startled boy roused his father to tell him about the dream. They went at once outside and started digging the well. When the hole was hipdeep, it filled with water. They carried a bottle of it to the bedside of an aunt crippled with rheumatism. She had not walked for years. They bathed her with the water and she walked across the room.

The news soon spread. Many came: the infirm, the crippled, and the blind, all hoping to be cured. There were those who did not believe and when they "boo-ed" at the well, the water dried up. The young healer would drive them away, look into the dry hole, and the water would rise again. So many sick people came for water, the well was emptied. It was often necessary to wait a spell for the water to rise again.

The city doctors had failed to relieve Josie's father of the rheumatism that warped his body, and he was now so blind that he groped his way around. He believed this "miracle" story and he wanted to try the cure at the well. Josie asked if she might take a vacation and go with him to La Union, to the miracle well. I did not mind her journey, but I was remembering the little statue of the saint far up in the Ilocos Notre country that wept the fake tears. There was our recent journey to Lipa when we saw no rose petals fall. I doubted there was an "Apo Iro" and a miracle well at Agoo.

When they started on their journey, I felt so sorry for them. I was certain it was a wild goose chase full of heartaches and disappointments. A week later they returned, and Josie related the following story: "We had to wait all day to see the boy, because he had to go to school and because he goes three times a day to the church to pray, and because many sick ones are before us. All of them he treat in the same way, and all of them he cure. He pounded herbs and grasses and bound them to my father's back and sick knees, then he mixes his spit with the mud from the well and put on my father's sick eyes. The next day the boy bathed my father with the water from the well. His knees got straight, and he asked for a crucifix that he could see on the table across the room."

I, a doubting Thomas, looked upon the old man who had stumbled blindly from my door a few days before. Now beaming, he stood before me holding out a gift for me, his prized pet fighting cock.

I do not try to explain his recovery; there may be many and various reasons why such things may or may not be true.

This I do know. Where many scoff, others kneel to pray.

Chapter Seventeen

I NOW OWNED a handsome red fighting cock whose moniker was Ilocos. It was after he was cooped up under our quonset hut that we had our first words with our neighbor, a high-ranking career man in the Embassy who lived next to us. Ilocos, the cock, assumed that all of the inhabitants in the Embassy Compound were rice farmers and should be up and headed for the rice paddies by four-thirty in the morning. So at this hour, he would vigorously flap his wings and let out a cock-a-doodle-do. Scarcely had his morning greetings ceased, when Neighbor was at his bedroom window swearing louder than Ilocos had crowed. Those occupants of the quonsets at the far end of the compound who had slept through Iloco's crowing, no doubt, were roused by Neighbor's wrath.

I heard the commotion, so I rushed downstairs to try to shush the rooster, even if I had to put a clothespin over his beak. I found Josie, Julie, and José tying Ilocos' wings behind his back. "Mom," said José, "It is the flapping of the wings that brings out the crow." After this disagreement with Neighbor, poor Ilocos was put to bed with his wings tied behind him. He was bedded down in a cardboard box covered with a piece of tarpaulin so he couldn't tell the time of day. But Ilocos knew. At exactly four-thirty he let out a croupy-like crow. José rushed over to Neighbor's quonset and hid under the window to see if the croupy

179

sound carried that far. When he returned, he said: "Mom, he snores louder than the rooster crows."

One day José tethered Ilocos out on the grass. The string was too long, so the rooster headed straight for Neighbor's garden and pecked the petals from the gardenia bushes. And did *he* stick his neck out: Right away, Neighbor stalked over and demanded that José wring that blasted rooster's neck, or he would report us to the Ambassador. And he was quite sure the Ambassador would just love a pot of stewed chicken for his dinner.

The situation went from a national affair to a family crisis when Huddy took sides with Neighbor. José must get rid of the rooster! I took sides with José; we would keep Ilocos! José was going to train him to be a prized fighter. José knew a good fighting cock when he saw one, and many a bird with legs less sturdy than Ilocos had been know to drawn a 2,000 pesos bet. My eyes grew big and wide; so did Josie's. So we all sat down and tried to figure out just how we could spend the 2,000 pesos. Soon, on paper, we were doing a flourishing business with one red rooster. José was to have cock stables of his own; Josie was to have a new sewing machine and go to dressmaking school; Julie would study to be a beautician. I was to be general manager.

With my new vice, a fighting cock, I hurried down to the library to read everything I could about this venture. I learned the sport was brought to the Philippines by the Spaniards and the Mexicans with the galleon. In the past four hundred years it had become as deep-rooted in the social order as Catholicism, the merianda, and the mustache. It had continued through the years to maintain its premier position in the national sports of the islands.

I found a passage written by José Rizal, the great Nineteenth Century Philippine patriot, and his description, so beautifully done, could not be better said:

"To keep holy the afternoon of the Sabbath one generally goes to the cockpit in the Philippines, just as one goes to bull fights in Spain. Cock fighting, a passion introduced into the country and exploited for centuries past, is one of the vices of the people, more widely spread than opium smoking among the Chinese. At the cockpit the poor man goes to risk all he has, desirous of getting rich without work. To the cockpit the rich man goes to amuse himself, using the money that remains to him from his feasts and his masses of Thanksgiving. The fortune he gambles is his own; the cock is raised with much more care, perhaps, than his son who is to be his successor in the cockpit, so we haven't anything against it. The government permits it and even in a way recommends it, by providing that the spectacle may take place only in the public plazas on holidays. This is done in order that all may see it and encourage it.

"The cockpit at Manila does not differ from those found in other towns. It consists of three parts. The entrance is a large rectangle some twenty meters long by fourteen wide. On one side is the gateway, usually tended by an old woman whose business it is to collect the admission fee. Of this contribution, which everyone pays, the government receives a certain per cent, amounting to hundreds of thousands of pesos each year. It is said with this money, with which vice pays its licenses, magnificent school houses are built, bridges and roads are constructed, and prizes for encouraging agriculture and commerce are distributed. Blessed be the vice that produces such results. In this first enclosure are the vendors of buyos, cigars, sweets, and food stuff. The small boys come along with their father's and uncles who carefully initiate them into the secrets of life.

"This first enclosure connects with another somewhat larger one; a kind of foyer where the public gathers while waiting for the combats. In this enclosure most of the fighting cocks are staked to the ground with pieces of bone or hard wood with cords tied to their legs. And here gather the gamblers, the devotees and those busy in tying the gaffs. Here they make agreements, they deliberate, beg for loans, curse, swear, and laugh boisterously. Here, some man fondles his chicken, rubbing his hands over its brilliant plumage. Another examines and counts the scales on the legs. They recount the exploits of the champions.

"You will see many mournful faces carrying by the feet corpses picked of their feathers, the same creature that was the favorite for months, petted and cared for day and night. Flattering hopes had been founded upon the fowl, but now nothing more than a carcass to be sold for a peseta or to be stewed with ginger and eaten that night. Sic Transit Gloria Mundi. The loser returns to the house where his anxious wife and ragged children await him, without his money or his chicken. All of that golden dream, all of those vigils during months from dawn of day to the setting of the sun, of all those fatigues and labors, there results only a peseta, the ashes left from so much smoke.

"In this foyer, even the least intelligent takes part in the discussion while the man of the most hasty judgment conscientiously investigates the matter, weighs, examines, extends wings, feels the muscles of the cocks. Some go very well dressed, surrounded and followed by partisans of their champions; others are dirty and bear the imprint of vice on their squalid features which anxiously follow the movements of the rich to note the bets, since the purse may become empty but the passion never satisfied. All countenances are animated; one never sees the indolent, apathetic, silent Filipino. All is movement, passion, eagerness.

"From this place one passes into the arena which is known as the Rueda, the wheel. The ground is surrounded by bamboo stakes. In the rear, reaching almost to the roof, are tiers of seats for the spectators or gamblers. During the fight these seats are filled with men and boys who shout, clamor, sweat, quarrel, and blaspheme. Fortunately few women get this far. In the Rueda are the men of importance, the rich, the famous bettors, the contractor, the referee. On the perfectly leveled ground the cocks fight. There is breathless silence. Will the families have smiles or tears; feast or famine?"

Today in the Philippines, cock fighting is very little different, except that the game cock aficionados are introducing a big sturdy rooster from Texas. These birds, flown over, are trained in the tradition of the best stables and often draw bets that run into four figures.

Now if I was to participate in this vice, a vice more widely spread than opium smoking, I was going to do it whole hog. I decided, after a careful study of cock fighting, that Ilocos should be trained. I certainly didn't want him dragged from the pit and his carcass sold for a peseta. He must be trained to fight like a gladiator; trained to protect himself against the gaffs of his opponents; trained to be a winner.

So José and I took off for Malabon where the wealthy owners had their fighting cocks trained. We learned these fine roosters were kept in air-conditioned cages which resembled dog kennels and each cage had a number over the door like a hotel room. There was a regular trainer assigned to look after the sanitation and the ventilation of the quarters. We found one rooster, tobacco red in color, a fierce shuffler flown over from Texas, that commanded a price that ran into four figures and rated a bet of the same proportion. We watched the trainer put "Flurry Eye," "Mugwump," and "Don X" through their paces. We watched the big red rooster walk a rope. A rooster trained in this manner, we were informed, is seldom rattled in actual fight. He is seldom put out of balance, and carries himself with a killing grace.

Another trainer breathed cigarette smoke upon the cock's head. This was done to stimulate its senses and to acclimate it to smoke-filled cockpits. Another group of roosters were tethered a meter apart and strained at their leashes to fight each other. Three hours of this exercise in the morning sun was enough

Vitamin D for the day, as well as splendid training. There was a special diet list, prepared by a dietician.

These prized roosters, given more care than the children in Malabon, were an eye-opener to me. Heretofore, all I knew about a rooster was—he was an asset to a henyard. When he grew too old for usefulness, his neck was wrung and he was placed in a pot to boil. After boiling him all day, he was still too tough to eat, so back home in the States, we fed him to Bruno, our dog.

But not so with Ilocos. He was a thoroughbred.

On our way back to the Embassy Compound, we stopped to buy cigarettes so José could blow smoke in Ilocos' face; we bought vitamins, gaffs and sheaths, and nicotinized pills. Now I was well prepared to take over the job as dietician to a rooster.

We decided it was not best for Ilocos' health that he should continue to sleep with his wings tied behind him. So each night José would put the rooster in a bamboo basket and go to Pasay to sleep at the barong-barong of his cousin, Juan. Ilocos could sleep in this room with José and be staked right beside his bed. And, when four-thirty came, he could crow his head off. It would be sweet music to the ears of all the neighbors. They would rouse and say: "Ah, a fighting cock!"

Each morning at sunrise, José and Ilocos returned. During the day, the rooster was tethered under the papaya tree with enough slack to permit him to peck at grass, leap high for grasshoppers, but not enough to reach the white gardenias in Neighbor's garden. Each day José put Ilocos through his paces. As a matter of fact, José did none of his houseboy duties. Josie and I were coconuting the floors while José taught Ilocos to walk a rope.

With vitamin pills, a diet, and exercise, Ilocos became a very handsome rooster. Even Neighbor, now mollified, came over to admire him and to give advice to José about placing good bets. Each day after sundown, Juan would come up and bring Mugwump, his rooster, and we would stage cock fights at the rear of the quonset over by the sea wall. In the ringside seats sat the new aficionados, Neighbor, and Huddy. You would have thought the rooster belonged to them. Ilocos got good training. He was raring for combat in the pit. The 2,000 peso bet was practically in our hands.

Everywhere I went—by bus, jeepney, or by taxi—I found myself discussing fighting cocks. Many times I stepped into a cab to find a Filipino in the back seat with a bamboo cage on his lap and in it a prized rooster. I'd say: "Oh, you are going out to Malabon for training?" Then I'd speak wisely to my companion as I discussed Ilocos' diet, exercise, and the likes. The Filipino was aware that I, too, owned a fighting cock, that José had the rooster down at Pasay for preliminary fighting, and that soon we would take bets on our rooster.

I stopped off for lunch at a Chinese restaurant over on Taft Avenue. It would be another hour before José would return home with Ilocos. I ordered chicken adobo with rice, a native specialty. While I was waiting for the Chinese cook to prepare my meal, I was startled by the sudden flapping of wings and the loud crowing of a rooster right in the cafe. I glanced around, half expecting to see a chicken pen in the kitchen. Perhaps I might select my own fowl as one selects a live lobster, and, while I waited, the chicken would be chased into the frying pan and emerge all adoboed. And, perchance, in this delicious mess of adobo, I might find a chicken foot bearing a little tin band—this would assure me it was the bird of my choice.

The rooster crowed again, then I spied him. Over in the corner of the restaurant sat two Filipinos. One was dressed in a slack suit of deep pink; the other wore a green suit. Each had a fighting cock tied to a leg of the table. One, a big red rooster; the other a Thompson white, tall, and sleek. They fed the roosters tidbits of rice and shrimp.

I had never minded a dog in a restaurant and I had often fed tidbits to my cocker spaniel under the table back in the States, but the sight of a rooster in a restaurant was different.

Why didn't the Chinese owner hang up a sign: "No Roosters Allowed"?

Suddenly it seemed to me the restaurant smelled like a chicken yard. When my adobo was placed before me, I turned over each grain of rice trying to find the tail feather of a rooster. At about this time, the big red rooster spread his pretty wings, strained, and deposited a pile of water-like droppings on the floor. I suppose there is no way of knowing when you need to take a rooster for a walk. No one was disturbed. Then the big Thompson white relieved himself. Several people passed by and paused to admire the fighting cocks. Soon the droppings became only a smear on the floor.

I could not eat my chicken adobo; I paid for the meal and took a taxi home. I was most anxious for José to return to find out just how Ilocos had stacked up during his preliminary fight.

When I entered the quonset, I smelled chicken boiling. No doubt Josie had been to market, but after my experience at the Chinese restaurant, I could not eat chicken again for a while.

I raised the lid of the pot and saw the big fat bird. On top was a stalk of celery, a bay leaf, several carrots, and a green onion, along with a piece of ginger. Josie always stewed chicken in this manner. I gazed for a moment at the muscled legs of the boiling bird—I didn't know why at that moment I should think of Ilocos. But I did. I kept gazing at the bird until Josie came in with José.

"Oh, Mom!" Josie was sobbing. "It is Ilocos!"

"Ilocos!" I screamed. "What is he doing in the pot? I thought he was in the pit!"

The red-eyed José, between great sobs, told what had happened. He and Juan had decided to unsheath the gaff and let the roosters have a good work out. José simply could not explain what had happened, except that Mugwump had flown at Ilocos with a fury and had ripped him wide open. His insides, bloody and dripping, had dragged upon the ground. José had gathered up the murdered rooster, stuffed his insides back in, and hurried home.

"Who is going to eat him?" I asked.

"Not us, Mom." Josie cried. "Maybe you and the doctor. I couldn't waste him."

"No, no, I couldn't eat Ilocos." I was sobbing loudly.

"Shall we give him to the Ambassador?" José asked, remembering Neighbor's threat.

"You should have buried Ilocos, feathers and all!" I said.

We began to prepare for Ilocos' funeral. José got the shovel and dug a deep hole under the papaya tree, for it was in the shade of this tree that Ilocos had learned to walk the rope; here he had spent many happy days pecking at the grass and chasing grasshoppers.

With the grave ready to receive him, we lifted his carcass out of the broth, celery, carrots, ginger, and all, and tied the half-stewed Ilocos in a clean tea towel. As we bore him to his bier, the grease oozed out and dripped on the stairway.

Gently, ever so gently, we placed him in the grave. José wept when he laid the gaff and sheath over the greasy tea towel with a stalk of wilted celery poking through; Josie and Julie sang the native "Planting Rice"; and I, in true island tradition, tossed white gardenia petals—from Neighbor's garden—mixing them with the good earth as José filled in the grave.

And just like that we buried Ilocos.

Chapter Eighteen

෴෨ OUR TRIP to the Big Rice Terraces and the Bontoc Country, the land of the Head Hunters, carried us to the extreme northern part of the island of Luzon, thus completing a circle of the archipelago. In making this trip we would travel deep into the heart of Huk territory.

Each morning the Manila papers headlined stories about entire families murdered by Huk raiders, houses burned, rice and sugarcane fields laid waste, and carabaos butchered for meat. We packed "Adam" with the medical kit, jugs of water, and a few supplies and set out. Tony, our driver, was simply scared out of his wits. But it was in line of duty, and Huddy was ready to go. When he made trips into Huk territory, he always exchanged his khaki shirt for a white one, or a flowered sport shirt "à la Magsaysay," for the Huks would fire on any khaki uniform.

Harvel and I went along on this trip, despite José's dire prediction: "Mom, the head hunters in northern province still take heads." Josie and Julie cried when they waved good-bye, and José made the sign of the cross. Would they ever see us again?

On our way to Baguio we had to make two stops: Clark Field and Cabanatuan. As we turned into the road leading to Clark Field, we heard rapid firing and came upon several truckloads of Philippine Constabulary, all heavily armed. And creeping through the fields were the Huks taking positions behind tall stalks of sugar cane. There was another exchange of shots.

The captain of the Constabulary, on seeing the official U.S. jeep, made a sign for the enemy to hold fire, then motioned us to pass through. Tony was so frightened he stepped on the gas and shot through the lines, but even so a bullet blasted out the tail light of the jeep.

Our mission accomplished at Clark Field, we were headed out for Cabanatuan, Nueva Ecija, to spend the night. The Huk fighting was in full swing and we were advised by the Constabulary that it would be safer if we proceeded to Bongabon-Baler instead, which we did. All through the night we heard the rat-a-tat of machine guns. To feel safer, Toney placed his mat by the door just inside our bedroom.

The next morning news came that forty Huks under Commander Mulong, of the 8th Huk Batallion, had staged a daring raid near the Gamilla sawmill, barely a kilometer from Bongabon, looting twelve houses, taking sacks of rice, clothing, money, and other valuables amounting to several hundred pesos. While the Huks were busy ransacking the houses, the Philippine Constabulary patrol arrived. The Huks immediately ordered the people to lie on the floor, face down, and keep quiet. The P.C., noticing the houses unlighted and quiet, silently left the town.

On the same night, at Malolos, two well-known persons were killed: Hermenegildo Pascual, the sixty-year-old lieutenant of Pingabayanan, Polo, and his wife, Vicenta. They were shot at Lingonan Bridge. The armed Huks had called at Pascual's home to ask for money and clothing. The couple had only one peso left, which they handed over. They had no more clothes except the garments on their backs, for they had been raided the night before. The armed men took the peso and asked the couple to guide them to the bridge which was a kilometer away. Upon reaching the spot, they told them to return to their home; when they turned their backs, they were shot down. Up and down the island of Luzon each day such horror stories made headlines in the papers.

We were advised not to start out for Baguio until nine o'clock in the morning, for by that time the night raiders would have gone to their hideouts, and we might get through safely. However, on this very highway near Bongabon-Baler, three weeks before, the Huks had staged a daring daylight raid and had killed a party of twelve. This story made international headlines, for among the murdered was Mrs. Aurora Quezon, wife of the late President Manuel Quezon; her daughter, Maria Aurora, known as "Baby"; and Philip Buencamino III, husband of Niña Quezon, another daughter.

The Quezon motorcade, consisting of eight cars including two jeeps bearing members of the Philippine Constabulary, was enroute to attend the ceremony of the unveiling of a marker placed at the birth spot of the beloved Manuel Quezon; this was sixty-two kilometers from Bongabon-Baler.

The ambush was sprung at ten-thirty in the morning. Mrs. Quezon was riding in the lead car, a Buick sedan owned by Mayor Ponciano Bernardo of Quezon City. The Driver was Lt. Col. Antonio San Augustin, assistant manager of the Philippine sweepstakes; seated at his right was Philip Buencamino; next to him sat "Baby." Mrs. Quezon rode in the back seat, directly behind the driver, with Major General Rafael Jalandoni and Mayor Bernardo.

The party was approaching Villa Aurora, still on Nueva Ecija soil, and was passing along a zig-zag road on hilly terrain when the lead car was fired upon. The major jumped out of the car, threw up his hands in a token of surrender, and yelled: "This is Mrs. Quezon's party." He was shot dead.

All passengers in the first car were killed, except Jalandoni. He reached for his gun as the Huks rushed the car and hit him on the head with the butt end of a rifle. He dropped to the ground and they believed him to be dead. The bodies were dragged out of the car and stripped of all jewelry. Jalandoni was robbed of his rings and wallet.

After the first volley of fire, which crippled the lead car, the Huks concentrated on the rear cars. The entire attack had been so sudden, the guards had no time to return fire. Only three of them survived. Captain Manalang and Corporal Silverton jumped beneath the jeeps. Several of the cars in the rear were able to make a swift U-turn and speed back to Cabanatuan to report the tragedy.

The identity of the ambush gang as Huks was established by the drivers of the Cabanatuan Lumber Company who had been ambushed at the same turn in the road earlier and had been detained until the attack on the Quezon party was completed. When the drivers were set free, one of the Huks said: "Now you can go on. Your white-haired Mrs. Quezon is dead."

The news of the death of the beloved Aurora Quezon shocked the islands, the Far East, and the United States. Mrs. Quezon was mourned by every foreign country. It caused political repercussions, with President Quirino suffering the brunt of the adverse effects.

The newspapers carried such statements as: "Doña Aurora has spent her life trying to help the poor." "No better evidence than the bodies of Mrs. Quezon and her daughter, Baby, and ten other people, prove the Quirino administration has failed to solve the Huk problem." "How can I vote for a man who, deep in my heart, I blame for the death of Mrs. Quezon?" The attacks ran on and on: "If the president would devote more time to serious work instead of sleeping so much." Again the 5,000 peso bed was brought into the story.

Those who were very close to Baby Quezon said she had had misgivings about making the trip into Huk land. For three nights Baby had dreamed of her father; in each dream he was beckoning her and saying: "Come with me." She had said to her mother: "Maybe I am going to see him soon."

"Pray for him," urged her mother, but even Doña Aurora had had misgivings about the trip. The morning they had set out, she had gone to early mass and received Holy Communion. Then she had placed in her handbag an old rosary with several beads missing; she believed the rosary had warded off certain harm many times. It had belonged to her mother; and she, too, had believed it had certain power against harm. Doña Aurora had not been able to snatch the rosary from her bag; the attack was so sudden. She also carried in her purse rose petals from Lipa that had been blessed by the Mother Superior.

The Republic of the Philippines buried Doña Aurora in North Cemetery on April 29, 1949, beside her husband, President Manuel Quezon. Over 200,000 people lined the streets of Manila to bid her farewell. Among them were high-ranking military personnel and dignitaries from foreign lands. Throughout the islands the Sun and Stars of the Philippines flew at half-mast.

Tributes and praise poured forth for this great woman who had built the Philippine Red Cross into the biggest chapter of this charity organization in the world. Ewald E. Selph, at that time president of the American Association of the Philippines, on behalf of the American community, recommended we go into a month of mourning. "She was the First Lady of the Land; she was the window of a great man. Her place in the Philippines was the same as that of Martha Washington in the early days of the American Republic."

José P. Laurel, one of the truly great men of the islands, said: "I join my countrymen in grieving over this national catastrophe. Doña and her daughter had been performing heroic works of faith, hope, and love for the masses in the noble tradition of our late President Quezon. Like him, they have given their lives in the course of a thankless struggle for the betterment of our people."

It was Doña Aurora's quiet, unobtrusive, self-effacing influence and example, her personal piety and conjugal devotion, that had helped Manuel Quezon carry through his program of social justice. She walked always beside her husband, and through the years she brought him a rich store of comfort and council and unfailing encouragement in his public career. She was a model of a Filipina wife and Filipina motherhood.

There is not an American soldier who served in the Philippines during the dark days of Corregidor that will not remember Baby Quezon. During the bombing of Manila, it was she and her friends who stayed on at Malacañang Palace to wrap Christmas gifts for the soldiers; gifts that had been collected by public subscription, with Baby heading the drive.

It was Baby and her sister, Niña, who volunteered their services to the Chief Nurse on Corregidor. They made beds for the patients and folded gauze for the operating room. This was not enough. Baby Quezon insisted that she should visit the front. But General MacArthur and President Quezon would not permit her to endanger her life. However, during the lull in the Japanese bombing, Baby was her father's constant companion on his trips outside Big Malinta Tunnel.

I shall always have a feeling of pride that I was called upon to write the eulogy for the United States of America for Doña Aurora. The Women's International League, of which I had long been a member, gave a memorial for Mrs. Quezon over the Philippine radio network. There were tributes from France, England, Australia, and from thirty-two other foreign nations. Many of the speeches were beautifully written and presented. Some were long; others flowery. I had written a very brief and very simple tribute for the United States. It had come out of my heart. I shall quote it:

"We, the women of the United States of America, join the women of the Philippines to humbly bow our heads in grief over the passing of a great woman—Doña Aurora Quezon. As we look down the path over which she traveled, we find her greatness was made up of little things: her radiant smile, the warmth of her soul, her friendly nod, her willingness to reach a helping hand to those less fortunate than she. We remember Doña

Aurora as a woman who always took the time to be kind, perhaps, even to those who hastened her death.

"It is true that this great woman is no longer with you. Yet no bullet could kill Doña Aurora, nor could it extinguish her light. Today, as we look down the path, her light is shining brighter than ever; a hundred years from today it will shine over these islands. And to you, our friends in the Philippines, we of the United States of America leave this word of comfort: Things that are good are never destroyed . . . and Doña Aurora was good. All the words of faith, of love, and of peace she has ever spoken will be carried on from generation to generation in the hearts of good people. The pattern of her life will be followed. And wherever human suffering finds relief, finds peace again, there, too, will be your Doña Aurora, her spirit soaring unleashed among her people."

After Doña Aurora's tragic death, the Huk Rebellion gained momentum. Up and down the island of Luzon, people were murdered and rice granaries robbed. The Huks had definite plans to take over Malacañang Palace. In order to accomplish this coup they must liquidate a long list of powerful men. Heading this list were Vice President Fernando Lopez, Carlos P. Romulo, the most influential man in the Philippines, and Ramón Magsaysay, the most beloved.

The people of the Philippines looked to Ramón Magsaysay, for he was the one man capable of saving their country from Communism. For this trained former guerrilla fighter knew how to reach the Huks, how to appeal to these misled people.

His record as Secretary of Defense in the Philippines is yet to be equaled. When he took over the job, there were 20,000 well-organized and well-armed Communist-led Huks that terrorized the outlying provinces. These rural areas were fertile ground for the Huks because the graft-ridden government cared little about the poor; it permitted a crooked Constabulary to abuse and cheat them. What could the poor farmer do? Many preferred to follow the Huks and their promises, rather than be cheated by their own government.

As Defense Secretary, Ramón Magsaysay relieved incompetent army officers, even against presidential opposition. He promoted the competent. He went straight to the core of the trouble, to the extent of giving financial aid to families of the insurgents. He promised amnesty and jobs to all who surrendered, and he lived up to these promises quickly and exactly. He set up furniture stores to give former Huk carpenters employment; he settled many of the one-time rebels on the fertile farmlands in Mindanao. In two years' time, the Huks had dwindled to a mere four thousand.

There were heartbreaking moments. Once the Huks retaliated by massacring every woman and child in his home town barrio. Ramón Magsaysay liked to think he was tough and ruthless, but his heart was pure gold. He had the strength of a bull, but after this horrible massacre he was so deeply touched and so shaken that for weeks he could not sleep.

Finally he captured one of the Huks who had taken part in the massacre. He didn't seek revenge by killing; that would not help. Patiently he talked to the man for hours, then said: "I still believe you can become a good citizen; I am going to give you a chance to prove it."

Ramón Magsaysay had seen, with his own eyes, men join the Huks because they could not make a living on the land. "You don't kill Communism with a sword and a gun alone," he said. "Communism is an idea. When a man with a hungry belly is working in a rice paddy on land which is not his own, always in debt, his children always hungry, well . . . the answer is clear. Someone whispers in his ear: 'Land belongs to the man who works it; come with us, we will give it to you.' My friend, something happens to that man. It is like a cool wind blowing through a hell on earth."

Chapter Nineteen

❦ WE ARRIVED IN BAGUIO just at sunset. There was a riot of color. The pine-clad hills surrounding the town appeared to be on fire. To add to this colorful scene, the sun was setting behind one hill and the full moon coming up over another.

Baguio, the summer capitol, one hundred and fifty miles north of Manila, is a little paradise nestled in the mountains of the Benguet province overlooking the plains of Trinidad. The elevation is five thousand feet. The days are seldom over sixty-five degrees, and the nights so cool you kindle a pine log fire in the big fireplace and sleep under a wool blanket.

Camp John Hay, the army rest camp, commands one of the most spectacular views in Baguio. I was awe-stricken as I stood on the rim of the hill and looked across the valleys to the distant purple-rimmed mountains.

The Country Club overlooking the Benguet Mountains has a view no less dramatic. This is the golfer's paradise, perhaps the most picturesque greens on earth. Here you may glimpse the colonel's lady dressed in smart golfing togs, wearing her best cashmere sweater, followed by an Igorot caddy wearing only a G-string.

This mountain paradise has never felt Jack Frost's icy fingers. The reddish-colored soil grows luscious fruits and vegetables: the largest and the sweetest strawberries that I have ever eaten; big red tomatoes of which, when sliced, one portion would cover a saucer; cabbages that would measure a foot and a half in diameter; and acres and acres of purple egg plants that resemble purple blossoms.

We stopped at Captain Keith's Guest House. This famous old place was owned and operated by a retired American Army Captain and his lovely Mestiza daughter, Lura. His Filipina wife had been dead many years. The captain came to the islands during the Spanish American War and, like many Americans, fell under the spell of the Philippines and remained. After retiring as a city official in Baguio, the aged captain decided to return for a three-month visit to his native State, Arizona. It had been forty years since he had set foot on American soil, and likely this would be his last visit, for he was now in his middle eighties. At one time he had thought Arizona the most beautiful land on earth; now everything was strange. He remained five days, then returned to the Philippines and his beloved Baguio, never to leave it again.

During The Occupation, the Keiths were driven from their home, so the Japanese could occupy it. The captain, Lura, and their dog, "Pee Wee," took shelter in a bomb hole in the hills just across the way. They existed almost entirely on camotes; even Pee Wee learned to relish this sweet-potato root, for it meant survival.

Captain Keith, not afraid of the old devil himself, had many a narrow escape. Once a group of Americans and Filipinos were on the hillside scanning the skies, hoping to sight an American plane, for day after day they had waited and watched. Suddenly there appeared a silver streak! When the captain distinguished U.S.A. on the plane, he yelled out: "It's an American plane!" A Japanese guard, close enough to catch the word "American," quickly summoned the captain before a Japanese court and accused him of plotting against the Japanese. That carried the death penalty.

"Sure," said the quick-witted captain, "I did speak the word

'American.' The guard just didn't hear all I said." What had he said? The court wanted to know! The captain stood very erect, 'I saw a plane up in the air, and I said, 'See that plane up there? Isn't it a beauty? It is a Japanese plane and it is ten times bigger and ten times faster than any American plane!' "

Ah! That was different. The grinning Japanese judge gave the old captain a package of good American cigarettes and sent him back to his hole in the side of the hill.

Very soon, however, the sky was filled with American planes. The Air Force started bombing Baguio to rid the city of the Japs. The Keith home was suddenly abandoned, and the Japanese camp on the hillside was deserted—the Americans were marching in.

The Keiths returned to their home, only to find it a pig-sty and the beautiful garden destroyed. They were trying to piece together odds and ends of broken furniture when the captain noticed several barrels on the hillside near the deserted Jap camp. He went over to investigate and discovered it was good American whiskey. He and Lura rolled the barrels down the hill and over to their home. When the American soldiers marched into Baguio, he set up a bar in his yard, using coconut husks for glasses.

The army band was playing and the Keith bar was the busiest spot in town. On the morrow, the empty barrels were rolled away and the captain counted the take. Three thousand American dollars. The profit was used to refurnish their guest house, to take up life where they had left off. The Keith Guest House, with its fine food and hospitality, became a popular place.

One day a houseboy brought to the captain's desk a program which had been left at the door. The boy told him it concerned a play to be given at the Club House.

"What's the name of the play?" the captain asked the boy.

"Lebber Gones. Bebber Gones," the boy replied, speaking in a very rapid tone of voice.

Even the captain didn't understand and asked the boy to repeat the name of the play.

Again came the rapid answer: "Lebber Gones. Bebber Gones."

The captain smiled as he handed me the program and I read: "Let Bygones Be Bygones."

Harvel and I shopped at the Baguio markets. The costumes of the dark-skinned Igorot women fascinated us. These barefoot women wore loose blouses and their long black hair, unbraided, reached their hips. Their skirts, made of a hand-woven material of red and white stripes, were wrapped sarong-like and held in place by a tight corset-like belt, a sort of G-string wrapped around their waist several times with the fringed ends tied at the back to swish like a cow's tail. These belts are used by the mountain women for maternity corsets. Harvel and I each bought a complete outfit.

We were to meet Huddy at Camp John Hay for lunch, so it would be great fun to dress as Igorot women and surprise him. We did. He looked first at our bare feet, then his eyes traveled upward even to Harvel's long hair stringing down her back; my hair was short.

"You girls go right back to Captain Keith's and get dressed for lunch. I refuse to take you into the officers' mess dressed in such a manner!"

We were crestfallen. But not for long. A two-star general came to our rescue. He thought we were two cute little tricks, so we entered the dining room on the arms of a general. The much-chagrined Huddy joined us when the general insisted.

We were on our way to the Big Rice Terraces deep in Bontoc and Kalingas territory. The Bontocs were inveterate head hunters and in years gone by were considered the wildest and most intractable of the tribes.

Just out of Baguio we met the mountain folk coming to market. Many of the women had tattooed designs—a snake, a man, or a spear, the same designs they weave in a G-string—that reached from wrists to elbows. One had copper bracelets on each forearm made of coils that extended almost to her elbow. She told us the bracelets had been heated to a certain temperature and slipped over her hands when she was a child. She could never remove them. Another woman smoked a copper pipe. We saw an Igorot girl wearing a G.I. cap. We wondered if the cap was all the soldier had left her, but when she turned, we saw the baby strapped on her back, a G.I. baby, no doubt.

Many of the Igorot women carried their babies papoose-wise; others carried them in front with a gunny sack for a sling. A baby nursed a mother's breast as she walked along with a big basket on her head. One old woman carried in her hand an anito stick. This fetish, made of a section of bamboo, is opened at one end and split up both sides. She carried the stick in her right hand and tapped it against her left forearm. This would keep the evil spirits away.

Some women carried huge vegetable baskets on their backs, made secure by a band around the forehead which is attached to the basket. The women leaned slightly forward to carry this load with no assistance of the hands. They can carry huge bundles of laundry on their heads, or bundles of wood, and climb the Baguio hills with the ease and balance of a tightrope walker, their hands free to carry other parcels.

The women also lead the dogs to market. Dog meat is considered a great delicacy in the mountain provinces. As the dogs trotted along, their bellies, stuffed with rice, almost touched the ground. For several days before this trek to the market, the dog was starved; then he was permitted to gorge great quantities of cooked rice. The buyer looked for this feature when he went to the dog market. The animal was bought, led home, killed and skinned, but the innards were not removed. When the dog was roasted, it was already stuffed with rice. The juices of the innards gave the rice a good flavor.

Behind the women came the men, completely naked except for a scanty G-string. Their dark bodies were tatooed from head to toe and resembled walking Persian rugs. They were bringing their wares to market: spears, head axes, bolos, and necklaces made of wild boar's teeth. Many of the men wore brass coils around their necks; these, too, had been placed there when they were very young. As a result, their elongated necks resembled the necks of giraffes. They also wore many brass coil bracelets and long coil earrings. One man had a long slit in his cheek near his ear, through which he slipped the stem of his pipe.

A vendor offered to sell me a head axe which he claimed had belonged to his grandfather, who had used it to whack off at least fifty heads. The axe didn't look very inviting to me since we were on our way to his grandfather's country. But nevertheless, Huddy bought it; he also bought two spears, another head axe, and a big bolo knife. Now we were fully armed to meet our foe, the head hunter.

The Benguet Igorots, unlike the Bontoc head hunters, are a kindly, truthful people, and faithful to a trust. Should you give an Igorot an errand to run, a valuable article or a message to be delivered, and you were sure he understood the order, he would be faithful to the trust even unto death. It was reported that during the construction of the Benguet Road, hundreds of thousands of payroll dollars were sent up the mountainside on the backs of these Igorots. The only loss incurred was the time an Igorot was waylaid by an American and robbed.

The Benguet Igorots are not a warring tribe; neither are the Lepantos nor the Amburayans in northwest Benguet. All are timid, patient, and hard-working people.

We were now headed for the mountains. "Adam" crept inch by inch over the perilous road to the Big Rice Terraces at Banaue —a road so narrow in places that one wheel dangled over the edge of a precipice. But we forgot to be frightened; the scenery was so breathtaking.

The Big Rice Terraces are listed as one of the Seven Wonders of the World. Any time a man might think he is bigger than God, he need only gaze over these awe-inspiring mountainsides and he will be cut down to size. At first I wanted to believe it was a fairyland, but I was brought to the sudden realization that these spectacular rice terraces were real. They climbed up sheer mountainsides like a great stairway to heaven, one terrace after another as far as the eye could see; mountain after mountain with every single foot of dirt, from the valley to the crest, terraced for the rice fields. There is no other place on earth that can boast of such an engineering feat; no modern soil conservation program can match it.

The terraces, built hundreds of years ago by the Filipinos, were made with stone, and all the work was done by hand. This engineering project is so perfect that seldom, if ever, does a terrace need to be repaired. The water is diverted into little streams that trickle from one terrace to another so as not to waste one precious drop. Each family in the surrounding mountainous country has a terrace; it is its farm. Here it plants and harvests its rice crop.

It was sundown when I first looked upon this masterpiece of engineering. The water which had flooded the terraces was now a deep pink color and the mountain peaks were tangled with fluffy pink clouds. We could see the Igorots wending their way, single file, down the mountain trail. The day's work was done. Their naked bodies, clad in G-strings, glistened like copper. Contentedly they smoked their pipes and seemed in perfect step like an army marching. They carried baskets on their backs and spears in their hands.

The women in this province wore the woven striped skirts but no covering above the waist, except, perhaps, many strings of beads. Many of them painted their bare breasts to beautify them, as we paint our lips. When an Igorot man says he has a pretty wife, he usually means she has beautiful, firm, brown breasts. He brags about them as an American man brags about his wife's pretty legs.

The high point of this dangerous mountain journey was to be invited to the big Igotor Canao to be held in the hills near the barrio of Bokod. This ancient ceremonial feast was ordained by Cabunian, the old Benguet god in Mount Pulog, in order that all people might share alike.

This Canao was being given by Mayor Dennis Molintas, incumbent governor of the mountain provinces. He had invited the people of twenty barrios and poblaciones as far as Kabayan, Itogon, and La Trinidad. Each of the invited groups had a designated place for feasting and dancing, and on the fifth and the last day of the Canao, they were given the head of a carabao or a horse to be carried home and butchered.

The institution of the Canao is a very important phase of old community life. Tradition required that a man, to be eligible for the favored circle of the bacnang, or wealthy class, and eventually to be eligible for the council or elders, must give a series of "Peshiets" during his life time. These are only preliminary feasts where a few pigs and small jars of home-brewed tapoi (fermented rice wine) are offered as a sacrifice. This achievement makes him worthy of old Cubunian.

This impressive Canao ceremony holds little interest for the younger and educated generations of the Igorots. The circle dance does not attract them; true, they are awed by the spectacle of entertainment, but the occasion has lost its religious meaning. Their attitude is very much like that of our younger American Indians toward their ceremonial dances. However, the attitude of the young Igorots is of great concern to the old people. They believe this indifference on the part of the young toward the Canao might have angered the old Benguet gods, and might have precipitated the Japanese war inflicted upon their islands.

The aged ones told us that in other days the Canao was very

fine. The sacrificial pigs were more mature with larger tusks; the ceremonial blankets were woven with much finer workmanship. As they spoke of these things, one of them pointed to a blue silk parachute, a discarded U.S. Army number, spread up high to shade the dancers. Such innovations were not allowed in their day. The blaring tones of a radio came from a nearby nipa hut. The old man shook his head sorrowfully and with his bamboo cane pointed in its direction, "We don't like that either."

However, according to the aged ones, the setting for the Canao had not changed in four hundred years. The nipa huts, grouped around a hardened clay yard, stood on frail bamboo stilts and were burdened with heavy thatched roofs. The huts were used as a combination home and rice granary. There were a number of old heirlooms that had been used in many a Canao: a century-old Chinese jar to hold tapoi, and some old brass gongs with a true ring.

The sacrificial pigs, with their four feet tied together, huddled in a pile on the hard clay ground, squealing and groaning as if they knew the intentions of the Benguet gods. The dancers did characteristic poses in a circle around the animals. The men had ceremonial blankets around their shoulders, and the women, fully dressed, wore blankets sarong-like. The circle dancers were followed by two brass gong players and they, in turn, were followed by a man beating time on two metal sticks. Over in the shade were two solibao players. The solibao is a bongo drum that resembles an American Indian tom-tom, except that it is twice the length. It is made of a slender hollowed-out tree trunk, very ornate with rattan weavings.

The "Mambunong," or high priestess, dedicated the squealing pigs to Cabuntan. She carried in her right hand a feather and in the left, a rattan tray. After the offering was made, the pigs were stabbed through the heart and while still squealing, were held over the fire to be singed to bring out the roasted flavor. Later, they were cut up in hunks and boiled in salt water.

The guests sipped tapoi, joined the circle dance, or listened to the religious chants by blanket-clad women who sat under the nipa huts. Huddy preferred to sip tapoi, but Harvel and I joined in the circle dance.

This Canao lasted for five days. The young women busied themselves at the rice pots, for there must always be plenty of rice; the small children and the wrinkle-faced old women sat around and listened to the wise old men pair off their children in marriage.

Since the old Benguet gods decree the Canao is a time of all people sharing alike, cattle and horses were butchered in the nearby villages and the meat distributed among the people who could not attend the ceremonial feast. Each family received no less than two kilos of meat.

From these peaceful and friendly Igorots we learned bits of news about the Kalingas to the north. In years past, the Spaniards transported a few Moros to the Kalingas country, and this fusion with Moro blood made them a very different tribe. They were war-like and had very strict moral codes. For instance, unchastity in women was punishable by death.

There always existed an enmity between the villages, especially in the old days when there were no roads. They lived each day for the next so they might feud with the tribes over the mountains, like the Hatfields and the McCoys in Kentucky. Their customs and manners were completely different. One village might put to death an unchaste girl; another might honor her for bringing forth a child. These feuds were handed down for generations.

We were told of an incident that happened in the central Bontoc school, where the warring villagers gathered to learn to read and write. One day a little boy approached the American teacher and said: "I think I am about to be murdered." The teacher, considering it only a passing remark, sent the boy out in the school-yard to play. A few minutes later, another small boy from a feuding village plunged a bolo, on order, through the stomach of the little boy. He died of the wound.

But we found the Kalingas now a kind and friendly people. We were invited to spend the night with the Alcalde of a barrio. His house, built on the side of a mountain, was surrounded by rice terraces. He told us many tales of the days, now gone, when the old ones did indulge in the game of head hunting. The warriors wore long hair tied in a knot at the nape of the neck and decorated with the curling feathers from a rooster's tail. Other plumes were fastened to a stick to stand high on either side of the head. The Kalingas' colors were red and yellow, even to their G-strings. Their bodies shone like burnished copper, and for armlets they wore the curved tusks of wild boars. A warrior carried a head axe tucked through his belt, with the naked blade resting against the bare skin of his thigh; he carried a wooden shield carved in a beautiful pattern of his own design and a long spear with the handle decorated with bands of brass and copper.

Our friend told us about the tribe to the north of the Kalingas, the Apayaos, the last of the tribes of northern Luzon to be civilized. In other days, this tribe of ferocious head hunters would take an enemy's head: a warrior, an aged one, even the head of a child. Everything was considered fair in this sport of head hunting. When a party returned from a successful head hunting trip, they would chop up the head of the victim into as many pieces as there were men in the party. Each hunter had a basket which was made by splitting the end of a bamboo cane, spreading the pieces, and weaving around it other pieces of split bamboo. When finished, it was a cone-shaped basket at the end of a pole. The stick was then driven into the ground and a small piece of the victim's head was put in each basket. These baskets lined the trail leading from the village where the head was chopped off. According to the tradition of the Apayaos, this kept the evil spirits away.

The next day, the alcalde and his wife took us to see a mock ceremony depicting the ancient taking of a head. There were eight "warriors" out to "take a head." They wore heavily carved shields to protect themselves from the "enemy." They advanced slowly toward a single man armed with a spear—the "enemy" didn't have a chance. In the old days, should they have taken his head, they would have chopped it up in pieces and divided it amongst the eight warriors who were participating.

The dance was centered around a head crudely carved out of wood and fastened to a post. Around the neck of this grotesque head were necklaces of wild boar's teeth and wreaths of flowers; there were also vicious-looking earrings made of wild boar's tusks. Directly under the head was the name "Makiling." This seemed to be a big joke, for we inquired about it and they all laughed. Then they informed us that it was the name of a murderer who had killed five mountain folk in a drunken orgy. He was now serving a life term in Bilibid prison. This was being done to shame him.

A dance was presented by a group of women—very young girls, an old wrinkle-faced woman and two young mothers with babies strapped on their backs. They would take turns and dance very gracefully right up to the head, then back away and let others take their turns.

Six men, gaily tattooed and heavily ornamented with brass bracelets and rings and wearing red and yellow G-strings, beat a weird rhythm on the solibaos. Another group of men and women lined up for a dance. The girls wore skirts of red and yellow, so narrow they scarcely met around their bodies, each with a belt tied at the back to dangle like a cow's tail. One girl would dance toward the head, then present the next dancer. This continued until the fifteen girls in the lineup had been presented. These beautiful dancers placed their hands on their hips and ran forward, then backward, in graceful movements, always keeping their feet very close to the ground in a beating rhythm.

The men dancers wore G-strings of navy blue woven cloth

trimmed with red. They had slim, copper-colored bodies. They took turns and danced in and out of the circle of women, following the leader, weaving a very pretty pattern. Their bodies were bent forward and their heels lifted high. The dance was presented always to the head of "Makiling" on the post.

After the dance there was a big feast of lechon, or roast pig, roast dog stuffed with rice, and preserved bananas. There was chanting among the old women, and marriage matches were made as the old men sat about in a huddle.

I was glad when the ceremony ended. It was weird and depressing, despite its beauty. As we jogged over the mountain road toward the alcalde's home, I was a bit uneasy. I knew head hunting was a thing of the past, yet I kept thinking of the young men who sat over the jars of tapoi drinking their fill. They were highly emotional by nature; just suppose they might get an idea to really re-enact the head hunting scene here on this lonely mountain road. Tony, our driver, must have shared my thoughts, for he gunned "Adam" and we took the mountain curves on two wheels. At other times I might have cautioned him to take care, but at this moment, in spite of the speed, it seemed that "Adam" was moving like a snail.

It was dark when we arrived back at the nipa hut on the mountainside. After saying goodnight to our host and hostess, we went to our room. Over in the corner were the weapons we had bought from the vendor in Baguio: two spears, two head axes, and a bolo. They might still come in handy. Just then there was a rap at the door. I rushed to Huddy's side, but it was only Tony wanting to borrow a spear. "Sir," he said rather sheepishly, "I'm not going head hunting, but sometimes animals come near after dark." He was sleeping underneath the hut near the jeep. Huddy gave him a spear, but assured him the day of head hunters was gone.

After we had retired, I kept reviewing the weird ceremony we had witnessed. Evidently everyone in the household was asleep for the hut was deathly quiet. Then the sound of the flapping of a bird's wings reached my ears. The flapping grew louder and louder as if the bird were beating against the bamboo shutters on the window. Then I heard the frantic cry of my hostess: "Aswang! Aswang!" Then a loud cry came from the terrorized lips of our host; even the children were crying out "Aswang! Aswang!" I jumped to my feet and shook Huddy vigorously. I bade him arm himself with a spear, for I was certain the head hunters had us surrounded. He wouldn't even bother to turn over. I could just see his head nailed to a post with a group of dancers kicking high their heels. He refused to get excited. I grabbed a head axe and, thus armed, I said in my best Churchill manner: "Very well, then I'll fight alone!"

While I was flourishing the head axe, the door of our bedroom was thrust open and a small boy rushed in to close our window. "Aswang!" he called out as he placed a saucer of salt and garlic on the window sill.

A few minutes later we were all huddled in the dark sala, and our host explained the peculiar behavior of the household. The aswang was a spirit, a great monster that assumed the shape of a nocturnal bird. It hovered at night around the homes of pregnant women. Through a window, or any opening, the bird might swoop in and force from the mother's womb the unborn child and hang its entrails on a tree. The rustling of a night bird outside the window had created this panic. The alcalde's wife was put to bed and Huddy gave her some medication to quiet her.

There are many superstitious beliefs in the mountain provinces. There were unseen beings that always lurked. One should never throw hot water on the ground without uttering a warning, lest one scald an "unseen being." Many years ago the father of our host had tossed a pail of scalding water on the ground. The next day, his eldest son, the alcalde's brother, developed a sickness that resembled burns made by scalding water. A witch doctor was called in to diagnose the case. His theory was that the "unseen being's" son was scalded by the water tossed on the ground, and so, likewise, the maladay was inflicted upon the boy. When he died, the witch doctor explained his death in this way: the "unseen being's" son had also died.

The most intriguing tale we heard that night was that of the "bales" disease. The barrio folk believe that "bales" are gospel truth and they can quote case after case to prove it. Certain persons are endowed with mysterious powers to transmit a severe stomach ache to others who come near them, similar to our typhoid fever carriers. When the bales carrier, or mang-babales, is tired or perspiring, his power has a double wallop, so they say. The carrier is aware these curious powers run amok in his innards, but he never knows on whom the pain may be in-flicted. Some people are susceptible; others are not. Should one see a mangbabales approaching, one need only call out "supla bales," and one will be immune. If little children are exposed, the mangbabales simply rubs their stomachs with spittle and they are cured. However, many a person gets the bales from an unidentified carrier; in such a case a bales specialist must be called in to cure him.

The old folk who live in barrio Anibong still tell the story about dear old Aling Plisia, who, with her husband, Mang Panong, had gone to Calumpang to help harvest palay. She de-veloped an intense pain in her stomach and had to be carried home. Her husband tried all the known remedies to cure her; he could not give her relief. He called in the old "herbolario," Mang Alipio, the herbman; neither could he give her relief. Finally, Mang Panong took his striken wife to a doctor in town who gave him an expensive prescription to be filled. After she took the medication, she still did not improve. She knew she must die. So did the neighbors. They even began to look about for a new wife for Mang.

Then one night, Aling Plisia dreamed she was stricken with bales from an unidentified carrier. The next morning she related her dream and Mang hurried away to find a bales specialist. The specialist cured her. She was soon able to help once more with the rice harvest.

There was another mangbabales, an old one named Takia. If she came upon a group of small children who forgot to call out "supla bales," and the little ones often did forget, she would take the time to lift the shirts of the children who came near her, wet her finger, and paint a red buyo cross just above the navel. When she performed this simple act, they would never, never get the bales.

We retired to our bedroom after listening to these old wives' tales. Our host cautioned us to keep the window closed and to let the saucer of salt and garlic remain on the window sill. I was no longer concerned with the "Aswang," for at this moment I had a severe stomach ache. Huddy was already in bed. I grabbed my stomach with my hands and said: "I think I have the bales."

He didn't even move. He just said: "Repeat 'supla bales' three times, make the sign of a red buyo cross just above your navel, take two aspirins, and come to bed."

Home again. Never did my little quonset by the sea look so inviting. Josie, Julie, and José were so happy to have us back! They had gone to the Malate Church each day to pray for our safe return. When we brought in the spears and the head axes, José's eyes grew wide. "Mom," he asked, "did you take a head?" He had taken inventory of our arsenal, complete with shield; it was that of a mountain warrior.

"José," I said. "Those horrible things happened a long time ago. No one takes a head these days."

He looked straight at me as if he knew I was wrong, or misinformed.

He was polishing up the bolo knife, and Josie and I were displaying the head axes on the wall, along with the spears, the shield, and the dog roast dipper that I had bought in Baguio, when the evening paper arrived. José, who had by now learned to read, was the first to spy the headlines.

"Three Decapitated Bodies Found Last Night in the Bontoc Country."

José looked at me all-wise. "Mom, they do still take heads."

Chapter Twenty

PERHAPS NOWHERE on earth is Good Friday so colorful as in the Plaza of the old Quiapo Church in Manila. On this day thousands flock to pay homage to the Black Nazarene, a life-sized figure of Christ done in blackwood. During World War II, so the story goes, this statue saved the famous old church from being destroyed.

When news of the "Bataan Death March" reverberated throughout the Philippines in 1942, many an anxious mother and wife lighted tapers to this "miraculous" image. Many vowed, in this desperate hour, to walk on their knees to Quiapo Church each Good Friday for the rest of their lives should their sons or husbands be returned.

The battle for liberation, which brought more suffering and death in 1945, was the supreme test for the Black Nazarene. Die-hard skeptics watched the roaring fire rage around this area. Just a stone's throw away, the Quezon Bridge was blasted to atoms, yet the Quiapo Church, shrine of the Black Nazarene, remained unharmed.

When the Americans advanced to Manila, in February of 1945, the Japanese hurriedly abandoned the north side of the Pasig and fell back on prepared positions in the walled city, Intramuros. As they retreated, the demolition corps wreaked destruction upon Quiapo and the surrounding districts. The fire, spread by the planted bombs, quickly leaped from one business place to another all around this area. But the historic old church, save for a few scratches, was unscathed.

Vast crowds gather around the plaza on Good Friday, a seething mass of humanity. Women are dressed in their finest ternos; men wear gay-colored slack suits of red, green, and blue, their small sons wearing matching suits; high dignitaries appear in their best barong-Tagalogs; and little girls look like fairies in their billowy dresses of embroidered organdy the colors of the rainbow.

Near the entrance of the church, the emaciated beggars, half-clad men and women, make a human chain, sitting close together on the ground the way youngsters cling to a sled. They watch the pennies dropping in the baskets at their sides as they count the beads of their rosaries. You may see a woman, sitting behind another, taking time out to pick lice from the head of her friend.

The church plaza is a market place, with the poor offering their wares hoping to collect pennies to drop into the collection box just inside the church. As Harvel and I pushed our way through the crowd, we came to a small boy sitting behind an orange crate on which was a box of moth balls—five for five centavos. The sign read: "Fixed Prize." I bought five moth balls, goodness knows why, except that I liked the dark-eyed boy. I dropped the foul-smelling balls into my shopping bag. Another boy was selling rice birds in bamboo cages. Harvel bought two. Another sold California prunes, seven for twenty centavos. I dropped seven prunes in with the moth balls.

Mountain women had come to sell an assortment of herbs. A root, when boiled in a tea, was guaranteed to relieve a woman of pregnancy; another root, resembling a coiled snake, was touted as a sure cure for rheumatism, gout, or malaria. I bought a root that looked like a rattlesnake for José. His grandmother suffered with chills.

A woman sold red and blue drawers for little girls and under-shirts for men, and right beside her another offered gilt-framed pictures of Jesus. Another aged one squatted beside a large puddle of dirty tallow scraped from dripping candles and patiently molded the dirty tallow into small candles. These she sold to the faithful for five centavos each. Next to the candle-maker sat a girl selling red fingernail polish to the vain. An old woman, on her head a basket filled with boiled eggs, milled through the crowd yelling: "Baluts! Baluts!" Behind her trailed a vendor with exquisite tree orchids suspended from a bamboo pole.

A girl wearing a black lace veil devoutly counted her beads. Approaching was a young man carrying a big yellow rooster, cut out of tin, nailed to a two-foot bamboo pole. "One peso for the rooster," he called out again and again as he waved the pole over the head of the praying girl. The spur of the tin rooster snagged the black lace veil. The last we saw, the rooster was wearing the veil and the girl, unmindful of her bared head, was moving slowly toward the church.

There was an endless line waiting to enter the church this Good Friday. Many, true to their promise, walked on their knees. We also wanted to enter the church with the throng and pay homage to the Black Nazarene. But by this time we resembled gypsy peddlers and Harvel's rice birds were twittering too merrily to say their prayers. We met a little girl who wanted the rice birds, and a little boy happily received our six balloons, and a grateful old man took the undershirt from my arm.

There was no one to whom to offer the moth balls, nor could I take them inside the church for the strong odor was to liquidate a moth, not a congregation. I tossed them on the ground and, looking up, noticed I was standing directly below a carved figure of Christ with leis of sweet sampaguita hanging from His outstretched hands. Such a beautiful offering! I felt ashamed that I had tossed the moth balls at His feet. When I reached down to recover them, I was so jostled by the crowd that I lost my seven prunes, a little wax figure of Christ, a pair of little girl's red panties, and even my shopping bag.

We edged into the long line and stood with bowed heads. The small children stood in line patiently with their elders and played with colored balloons. It took hours for the line to move inside the church. The young and the old moved inch by inch to reach a small statue near the door to kiss its hand. The crowd moved on; it swayed; children were caught between grownups and cried out in fear of being crushed. Anxious parents stretched out their hands to protect them. Some hoisted the small ones to their shoulders so they could get a breath of air.

After hours of pushing and shoving, Harvel and I found an opening and made our way to the front door. A young man on the steps thrust a racing ticket under my nose. "Buy from me, Mom. This is a lucky ticket!" Suddenly I was angered, for I had just witnessed such devotion, so many prayers, so many tears. "Do you think I would buy a racing ticket on the threshold of this church?" He seemed surprised that it mattered where one bought a racing ticket. "Well, then, Mom," he said. "I will walk with you down there." And he indicated the church plaza where we might negotiate our trade.

An aged woman with a prayer book looked at me, then said to the boy "Begone. 'Tis Good Friday!"

On this holy day, from high noon until three o'clock, a weird passion play called "The Way of the Cross" was held in the picturesque village of Capitagan. This play was very realistic. In the drama a man, impersonating Christ, was dragged along the street while the rabble flung stones and cursed him. The protagonist was Rustico Santos, a frail, humble, highly esteemed farmer in his early forties who had played the part for a quarter of a century. The story goes that a sickness in his youth had caused him to participate in this passion play.

The players were dressed in costumes like those worn in the

days of Christ. Santos was swathed in a striped robe with a crown of thorns on his head. His long beard was made of abaca hemp dyed a dark brown, but the flowing hair was his own. The procession set out from the barrio church to lead the Christ to a rice field. Here he was dragged, buffeted, kicked, and clubbed until his body was bruised and bleeding. At this stage the rabble clothed him in a heavy, thick robe and burdened him with a wooden cross on his shoulders. He was dragged along the streets for a distance of eight kilometers by the jeering crowd who continued to stone him. He fell again and again as the crowd jeered. On this long journey he met the "Virgin Mary," and also a kind man, "Simon of Cyrene," who assisted him with his burden, and the bloody sweat was wiped from his face by another kind woman, "Veronica."

Rustico Santos was "crucified." His torso and shoulders were tied to the cross, he firmly grasped spikes at each end of the cross piece, instead of having his hands pierced with nails. The cross was raised and stood by the side of the chapel for the multitude to behold. When Santos "died," his body was loosened and the cross lowered. The soldiers, in loud colored uniforms, helmets, and snub-toed G.I. shoes, plagued Santos and lashed him heavily as he reclined on the ground.

On another Good Friday I went to Malolos to watch a Penitente procession. These flagellants lash themselves in much the same way the Penitentes scourge themselves in the remote mountainous regions of northern New Mexico. However, in the Philippines, this order will permit visitors to follow the procession and also to photograph it. Not so in New Mexico, where the rites are held in great secrecy, and to invade them is to risk one's life. I was at Malolos at break of day with my camera loaded with color film to follow the procession.

The Penitentes paraded single file down the streets of Malolos. The marchers carried long whips made of strips of inner tube to the ends of which were attached pieces of broken glass. This cat-o'-nine-tails thrown rhythmically over the left shoulder tore great chunks of flesh out of their backs. The men, stripped to their waists, wore white muslin trousers, which were dripping with blood. Over their heads were pulled white hoods, topped with a crown of thorns.

Each Penitente has a whipper that follows him in the procession, and should he fall to the ground from exhaustion, the whipper grabs the cat-o'-nine-tails and revives him with many lashes.

One lone Penitente lashed himself unmercifully until his back was raw. At each Station of the Cross, he fell exhausted, face down and arms outstretched in simulation of The Crucifixion. As he lay prostrate, his follower rushed over, picked up the fallen whip, and laid many a blow on his bleeding back. Again and again the Penitente struggled to rise, and when he reached the chapel, fell exhausted, but goaded himself on inch by inch, crawling toward the door. Again the whipper laid blow after blow on his bleeding back. The Penitente never whimpered, never flinched. Finally, he rose to his knees, picked up the whip, and gave himself a couple of strokes, then fell again. He tried to rise, but could not. Again the whipper laid lashes on his back.

Two attendants came forward with an instrument of torture, a small block of wood with a knife blade attached to each end. The blades were about six inches long and razor-sharp. One man held this double-edged knife in the small of the Penitente's back, while the other weighted it with his foot until it cut deep into the flesh. When the knife was removed, there was profuse bleeding. A third man poured a cup full of salt in the open wound to lessen the flow of the blood.

I could no longer watch the scene. I must seek shade before I, too, fell face down, beside the Penitente. I remained several minutes under the shade of a nearby mango tree, but was deeply concerned over the plight of the bleeding man. "Has he made it to the chapel, yet?" I asked a Boy Scout nearby.

"Mom, I think he must be dead. He has not moved since they cut his back with the knife."

The boy informed me the Penitente had scourged himself because he had miraculously escaped from Japanese captors during The Occupation. He had promised himself to endure this ordeal for five consecutive Good Fridays. Another Penitente who had recovered from a serious illness two years previous, also vowed to do penance for five years.

I followed the Penitentes to the seashore. Many, having completed the day of penance, plunged into the salty water to wash the blood from their backs.

This remnant of flagellants belongs to a vanishing cult which believes salvation lies only through severe, self-inflicted physical suffering. This gory imitation of the Messiah's pre-crucifixion travail was brought to the Philippines by way of Mexico where certain cults practiced a virulent form of self-punishment.

"Flagellants in religion," according to the Encyclopaedia Britannica, "is the name given to those who scourge themselves by way of discipline or penance. Voluntary flagellation as a form of exalted devotion occurs in almost all forms of religion. Flagellation had its origin in antiquity. Herodotus recorded it to be the custom of the ancient Egyptians to beat themselves during the annual festival of Isis. In ancient Greece at Alea the women were flogged in the temple of Dionysius. In the Christian Church, flagellation was originally a punishment which was practiced by parents and schoolmasters on erring children. It was practiced by priests and bishops in the castigation of erring priests and monks.

"The practice gradually found merit among the Christians during the medieval age and was even extolled as a virtue by many of the Monastic orders of the West. The early Franciscans punished themselves with extreme rigour. The flagellant brotherhoods were the outcome of a spontaneous popular movement and their sources of origin are very difficult to trace. They became widespread in Europe despite church bans."

It was sundown when I arrived home from Malolos. I was completely exhausted. My brown and white seersucker suit was splattered with blood, as were my feet and my camera. I looked as if I had participated in the stabbing of a sacrificial pig at a Canao. José was sure I had been attacked by an angry carabao, and Josie quickly stripped off my clothes to examine my back, no doubt fearful I had felt the lashes of a cat-o'-nine tails.

I simply could not eat meat for a week, but I got no sympathy from Huddy or Harvel. I should stay away from such sadistic spectacles! However, as I reviewed the events of the day, gory as they had been, I was still glad that I had seen this Penitente procession and had brought home priceless color film. I recalled another one of my "escapades," also a memorable one, but far different.

I had flown to Hong Kong from Manila to visit Ming Chua, a Chinese newspaper woman I had met on several assignments. I was informed when I arrived that we were going to the Chinese cemetery on this day, November 1, for "The Feast of the Dead," their equivalent of All Souls Day, to be held for this family at the tomb of "Third Uncle," and I was most anxious to observe the ceremony.

At the appointed hour, I tripped down to the lobby of the Repulse Bay Hotel to meet Ming. I wore a tweed suit, black gloves and shoes, a tiny black beret, and a somber look. After all, we were going to visit "Third Uncle's" tomb. But Ming was dressed in an elaborate brocade, made Chinese style, and all a-glitter as if we were going to a cocktail party. She looked me over, from head to foot, and I sensed something was wrong. "Am I not properly dressed?" I was not. I should wear my best dress for this occasion. So we returned to my room and quickly zipped me into a black cocktail dress with a string of glitter beads, my red velvet coat over my shoulders, and we set out for the cemetery.

Perhaps you've seen Christmas Tree Lane in Hollywood in all its gaudiness; it couldn't hold a candle to this Chinese cemetery on the outskirts of old Hong Kong. Many of the tombs were elaborate pagodas, and "Third Uncle's" resting place was no small edifice. It was a long concrete slab about three feet high, in the center of a beautiful open air pagoda painted Chinese red. The pagoda was lighted like an American home in a Christmas lighting contest; prayer papers were fluttering everywhere.

The entire family, including the children, wore rich brocades. The window, "Third Aunt," was elaborately dressed and appeared very happy. Even "Third Uncle's" concubine was there, dressed in rich brocade, as she crouched behind the tomb, ignored by the family.

The tomb was covered with a long linen table cloth, beautifully embroidered. At the head of the tomb was an enlarged photograph of the departed one, and by it a bottle of Scotch. The elaborate spread for "The Feast of the Dead" included large prawns cooked in butter, century-old eggs, pancit, sweet and sour pork, fruits, hot breads, and many pastries—all the varieties of food he had liked best during his stay upon this earth.

No one sipped from "Third Uncle's" bottle of Scotch, but there were cocktails for all of us, and for the many friends who came from other tombs to call on the family. All were making merry, for after all, this was the night the spirit of the dead returned. A band of musicians strolled through the cemetery to play request numbers; when they paused at "Third Uncle's" tomb, they were given coins to play his favorite tune, "The Last Time I Saw Paris." I was reminded that this was also one of the favorite tunes of José Reyes, the poor rice farmer back in the

Philippines whose funeral Huddy and I had accidentally come upon.

It was near midnight, and I was very hungry. Why did we wait so long to eat? The prawns had grown cold, the pancit was now sloppy, and the eggs a bit older. I didn't exactly relish the idea of being served from the tomb of a dead man, but I was so hungry I could have eaten the table cloth. I waited and waited. But we did not eat.

At the stroke of twelve we departed, leaving behind the elaborate spread so "Third Uncle" could partake of it as soon as we were out of sight. As we were leaving, a friend of the Chinese family chided my hostess. "Say, when do you think 'Third Uncle' will come down to eat all that good food?" My hostess had a brilliant sense of humor. "At the same time your departed one comes up to smell the flowers you left on his tomb."

Chapter Twenty One

WE HAD BEEN INVITED to Macabebe, a barrio seventy-five miles north of Manila, an historic spot, dear to the hearts of Americans. For here was organized the first volunteer company of Filipinos to come to the aid of the Americans in the Spanish-American War. Each year the old veterans and friends held an annual celebration of this event, and on this occasion a group of Americans had been invited as special guests.

We were met at the edge of the barrio by a remnant of Spanish-American War veterans, the Stars and Stripes, the village band, and a large crowd of people, the men in barong-Tagalogs and the women wearing their colorful ternos. After the official welcome, we were escorted to the residence of the alcalde for a day of feasting.

The large house, made of sawali, was covered with cadena de amor and bougainvillea. It stood on high bamboo stilts like all the other houses in the barrio. As we approached the front porch, we noticed bamboo baskets hanging underneath. These, we were told, were coops in which the chickens were put to bed each night to protect them from raiding varmints, or thieves.

Huddy entered the house with our host, but Harvel and I walked over to a barbecue pit to watch the young men roast a pig, which would soon be served as lechon. A bamboo pole was rammed through the eviscerated carcass from mouth to tail. The ends of the pole rested on saw horses. A boy squatted at each saw horse slowly turning this bamboo spit over a very small fire. It took a whole day and night to prepare the lechon, for the skin must be as crisp as cracklings, but never scorched.

The Filipinos love the history of their islands. When we entered the house, a group of old timers briefed us on the capture of General Aguinaldo, an historic event which had made Philippine history, and which was the occasion we had come to celebrate.

They recalled the battle of Tirad Pass, the last encounter between the Spanish-ruled Filipinos and the Americans. Major March and his battalion, riding for their lives in pursuit of General Aguinaldo, were halted at the Pass by the Presidential Guard under the leadership of twenty-two-year-old General Gregorio del Pilar. It was a long and bitter fight, and ended only when the Americans outflanked the Filipino barricade and annihilated the Guard.

The Spanish-ruled Philippine Republic was laid low at this rocky barricade thrown across a lonely trail, but not until the soldiers had fought to the bitter end with sticks and stones. The old veterans remembered the young general had ridden his white horse with quixotic gallantry into enemy fire, only to die for a cause that was already lost. But this brave stand had saved General Aguinaldo who was resting up in camp fifteen miles away.

After this skirmish the Americans lost contact with the fugitive general, and the war entered its third and its last stage of guerrilla warfare. The Filipinos kept an underground government and an army throughout Luzon, and so effective was this guerrilla fighting force that the American losses were doubled; the strength of the Army of Occupation was brought up to 70,000.

In 1901, General Arthur MacArthur, father of General Douglas MacArthur, was placed in command of the Army of the Philippines and served as military governor of the islands. In his effort to capture General Aguinaldo, he organized scout units, composed of Filipinos, the men from Macabebe, and former members of the Spanish Army. It was the Macabebe soldiers, under General Frederick Funston, who captured General Aguinaldo in March 1901.

The capture of sly, old Aguinaldo, an historic event, was accomplished through treachery and deceit. The general was hiding in Palawan when he dispatched a courier with coded instructions that he needed a force of four hundred men at his hideout. The courier was betrayed by a pro-American major who had the code of instructions deciphered by a Spaniard and sent to General Funston. General Funston disguised eighty Tagalog-speaking Macabebes as soldiers of the Republic and put them aboard the *Vicksburg* at Casiguran to sail to the island of Palawan. The Presidential Guard, believing they were their reinforcements, greeted the soldiers very formally, and while they were presenting arms, the Macabebes fired upon them. The Spanish spy who had deciphered the instructions captured General Aguinaldo.

General Aguinaldo was brought to Manila and treated like an honored guest rather than a prisoner. He was installed in a spacious house near Malacañang Palace by General Arthur MacArthur. The captured general then issued an order to his men: "Enough blood, enough tears and desolation." When he had made known that he had taken an oath of allegiance to the United States, very shortly every Filipino leader of importance on Luzon surrendered.

General MacArthur proclaimed an amnesty and a bounty of thirty pesos for each weapon turned in, and so the long bloody war came to an end. American sovereignty reigned supreme. The hatred engendered by the war soon disappeared, and the Filipinos joined the Americans in a program to lay the firm foundations for civil administration and economic development; these were education, law, defense, and prosperity.

When the new Republic of the Philippines celebrated its

independence on July 4, 1946, the eighty-eight-year-old General
Aguinaldo marched in the parade and no one stepped more
sprightly. Until his death he lived in a large pink house at Kawit,
near Cavite, within sound of the church bells of Manila.

Any Filipino feast is one you never forget, and the feast at
Macabebe was the most sumptuous I have ever seen. As I sat in
the spacious sala, I could see the servants in the kitchen. There
were at least thirty women busy with the cooking, one to prepare
each dish. Some of them were standing over the stoves watching
the pots boil, others squatted on the floor smoking little black
cigars, hind part before, as they cleaned large prawns.

The table was elaborately spread. In the center was the roast
pig, lechon, the favorite dish; then there were large stuffed fish
so artistically garnished that it seemed a pity to eat them; beyond
these were stuffed chicken, pickled oysters, prawns, chicken
adobo, and lumpia, the national dish; and finally, mangoes,
avocados, and dozens and dozens of dishes of fresh vegetables.

One native dish that fascinated me was the platter of snipes,
very much like our quail. These boiled birds, defeathered up to
their necks and down to their knees, were served on a large
circular bamboo tray. In the center of the tray was a large mound
of steamed rice. The snipes, with toes to the center, had their
feathered heads outward, with all the beaks turned in the same
direction, and their eyes closed as if they had just said: "Now
I Lay Me Down to Sleep."

Outstanding in this festive spread was a large basket of baluts.
For the first time I saw a balut eaten, and learned it is a duck
egg that has been hard boiled just two or three days prior to
time of hatching.

You eat baluts by peeling off the shells, sprinkling on a dash
of salt, and then chomping down on heads, tails, innards, feet,
topside, bottomside, and inside. The balut is a great delicacy, and

no young man would think of taking his best girl to the races, or to the movies, without a few baluts and a little package of salt to go with them.

The balut industry in and around Manila is said to be the only one of its kind in the world. It was started in the small towns that border Laguna de Bay, particularly in the towns along the estuary of the Pasig River. The balut industry in the town of Paternos, Rizal Province, employs several thousand people. To process a balut, duck eggs are placed in wicker baskets filled with heated, unhusked rice grains. It takes twelve days of incubation to produce nice tender eggs. Vendors buy the incubated duck eggs at Paternos for twenty-five pesos per thousand. They are brought to Manila where they are hard boiled. Customers pay one peso for three baluts. A vendor usually makes ten pesos per day, a good living.

Every American is supposed to eat at least one balut before leaving the islands. Time after time I tried to gather courage for this ordeal. Perhaps if I should swig down five glasses of tuba, rice wine, and then hide in a dark closet, I might be able to chomp down on a balut. One afternoon, just about the time I was sure I might attempt this feat, I saw an aged woman buy a balut from a street corner vendor. She bit into it and the entrails of the unborn chick dangled over her chin. She sucked them into her mouth—head, eyes, beak, and all—and then licked her lips to gather in the tiniest bit of this delicious morsel. I never did have the courage to eat this "delicacy."

All during the sumptuous meal at the alcalde's home, I kept hearing "Oink! Oink!" When I questioned my Filipino dinner companion, he said: "Oh, those are the pigs under the kitchen."

After the meal I was invited into the kitchen to see the native stoves on which our food had been prepared. I watched a Filipina woman scrape the food from our plates, and as it fell through the cracks in the bamboo floor, three fat pigs delightedly ate the scraps.

There is always entertainment at a Filipino feast. Our gracious host had Tinikling dancers perform for us. In this exciting dance, a barefoot couple jumps in and out of clicking bamboo poles. The poles, about ten feet long, are placed on two-by-fours lying on the ground about three feet apart. A Filipino lad sits at each end and holds one pole in each hand. When the music starts up, they bring the poles together with a click and then quickly separate them again, back to their original position. The dancers, a girl on one side and a boy on the other, with grace and rhythm, jump in and out of the clicking poles. An experienced dancer never gets a toe caught between the clicking poles. Harvel and I tried the Tinikling, much to the amusement of the young folk. At first we got our toes smashed a time or two, but we soon were able to jump in and out of the clicking poles. The rhythm is very much like that of rope jumping.

The day at Macabebe is one I shall always remember. There was such a friendly atmosphere, and there was peace among the good people of the barrio. Just at sunset, we left to return to Manila. We stood on the steps of the alcalde's gracious home and, arm in arm with the aged veterans of Macabebe, joined in singing "God Bless the Philippines."

Chapter Twenty-Two

EVER SINCE MY ARRIVAL in the Philippines, the nipa huts had fascinated me, from the tiniest hut—one room was often housing for a family of six—top heavy with its thatched roof, to the elaborate hut with mahogany floors and window panes made of mother-of-pearl shells. The nipa hut is cool during the hot weather, for the air penetrates the leaves of the roof and walls. Yet when the monsoon winds howl, the air spaces swell up with moisture and for a protection against the rains. The nipa hut belongs to the Philippines; up and down the islands this building material is used for homes, churches, schools, hotels, and cock pits.

When Huddy received orders to go to Cagayan to examine a veteran, I was pleased, for this was the land of nipa. The Cagayanos inherited from their forefathers the art of nipa making. When the Spaniards first came to this part of the islands, they found the people making nipa shingles for their "Amingans," or typical huts. We went to Aparri, Cagayan, located on the northern tip of Luzon on the Babuyan Channel at the head of the Rio Grande de Cagayan. This entire region abounds in swamps, which makes it favorable for the nipa palm and convenient, because the boats which carry the nipa to market can be floated down the river.

The barrio folk spend the entire year turning out shingles by the thousands. They have spent a lifetime at this industry, as important to them as the lumber industry is in our country. Even the poorest of the barrio folk may engage in the making of nipa shingles and thereby support their families. There is great demand for these shingles, for during the typhoon season some roofs are blown away, and others often need to be patched up before the rainy season sets in.

Our friends, the Valenzuelas, who lived in the barrio of Linao, gave us an inside story of this great industry. Mr. Valenzuela and his fourteen-year-old son, Nick, went each Monday up the swamp to cut nipa, and on this day they asked Harvel and me to go along. We donned khaki shorts, sweat shirts, and tennis shoes, for we had to wade in water knee deep to reach the nipa grove. We wore big hats made of nipa leaves to protect us from the blazing sun. Our host and his son wore khaki undershirts and shorts, large straw hats, but no shoes. They had waded these swamps all their lives and the soles of their feets were as tough as the pads on the foot of a jungle beast.

I felt a bit awkward wading along in my shorts, for in the barrios a Filipina woman never appears in such apparel. If she should wade the swamp, she simply pulls her full skirts high above her knees and twists them sort of trouser-like. I could see no difference; her knees were bared the same as mine. Perhaps I was shy because Josie never approved of my going around in shorts, even in the garden. She was always chasing me with a skirt hanging on her arm; should I answer the door in shorts, as I often did, she was right there wrapping a skirt around me before I could greet my visitor. Harvel *was* permitted to wear shorts according to Josie's standards.

As we trudged along in water, often hip deep, I kept an eagle eye out for alligators lurking under nipa palms; this swamp land was a natural habitat for them. We reached the nipa grove to start Monday's gathering. This same routine is following Monday after Monday, the year round.

The men, with great care, cut the palm leaves with their

bolos. The leaves are bundled into an uyon; this is one hundred nipa shingles of the commercial size. We helped to tie these leaves into a bundle that resembled a bundle of Iowa fodder. On Monday the men gathered enough leaves to last them through the week, and also cut a supply of tubu, the young, unopened shoots.

Nick was returning to the barrio by noon, so we decided to go with him. We each shouldered a large bundle of nipa leaves and waded down the swamp. Twice I fell down, dousing myself and ducking the bundle of leaves. I couldn't very well watch my way, for I was still watching for an old alligator. I was overly cautious, since the morning paper carried a story of a small girl, in a nearby area, who had been swallowed by an alligator. Of course, it would take an old whopper with huge jaws to slide both me and my bundle of uyon down his throat, but every time a nipa leaf tickled my neck, I yelled for help. We were glad to reach the barrio and the kind shade of the hut.

Monday's work was done. The bundles of nipa were stacked against the house, as we might stack bundles of fodder at a barn. They have a clean, sweet smell. It is a good life, and by this labor these Filipinos earn their daily bread.

Tuesday's work was begun. The Valenzuela family busied itself cutting and separating the binanucan, which is made of the midribs of the tubu. This thread is used to sew the leaves together. The young leaves of the tubu will be used later to tie the bundle of nipa shingles. On Tuesday the family cuts wild bamboo poles of the exact commercial size. On each pole are woven one hundred nipa palms.

From Wednesday until Saturday the family gathers under the shade of a tree to start sewing nipa. Sometimes the neighbors join in to help; it is a sort of nipa sewing bee. Everyone squats on the ground. With the bamboo stick for support, the leaves are sewn overlapping one another with the tubu thread. An expert nipa maker can finish two-hundred and fifty shingles in one day; beginners usually turn out around one-hundred and twenty. I made five!

After the nipas are sewn, they are laid on the ground, as neatly as shingles on a roof, to dry in the sun. Dried nipa commands a much higher price on the market, for it is very light and does not decay when stored. After the shingles, which contain one-hundred nipa leaves, are dried, they are then tied into bundles of fifty, using the young leaves for binding. This finishes a week's work in the life of a nipa worker. The nipa shingles will be loaded on a boat and transported down the river to market. The next week the same routine will be followed—the next and the next—for a whole lifetime.

Our next trip was to Manaoag, Pangasinan, to see the water wheels of Lauer—three gigantic wheels, seven meters in diameter, that resemble huge ferris wheels at a state fair and are the motor of an ancient irrigation system. The water wheels of Lauer stands on the banks of a river whose source is far up in the Benguet mountains and are run by the power of the river's water. The wheels, are constructed of seasoned bamboo and each wheel was, in days previous to the war, connected with bamboo tubes or pipes supported by prop-like perpendicular poles which elevate these primitive pipes to carry the water to five barrios for irrigation. Old timers will tell you that the water wheels of Lauer are older than the Manaoag Church built by the Spaniards centuries ago.

These ancient wheels are an institution; the barrio folk refuse to tear them down. Shortly after the liberation, the G.I.'s came to the barrio of Lauer to see this irrigation system. They watched the great bamboo wheels turn slowly in the river and lift water through bamboo tubes to distant barrios. The soldiers were amazed at this ancient mechanism, but, being efficiency minded, they offered to install an electrically-run generator, since there was a surplus left from the army. The citizens rose up in arms.

No sir, they would not part with the ancient wheels which had served them for centuries. They argued with the soldiers: suppose the electrically-run generator broke down; suppose the power went off. Not on your life would they trade! However, they did accept G.I. pipes through which to conduct irrigation water to the various barrios.

The irrigated crop in this area is neither sugar cane nor rice as one would expect to find; rather it is lauer, (ikmo in Tagalog). The tender, young lauer leaves are very popular with the buyo-chewing folk of northern and central Luzon.

Another bamboo treasure is the old organ in Las Piñas Church near Manila. This famous organ is pictured in the history books of the islands, and on travel brochures. People who have but a day or two of port-call in Manila hurry out to see the old bamboo organ, the only instrument of its kind in the world.

The construction of the organ was started in 1818 by Father Diego Cera, a member of the Augustine Recolets Friars. The nine-hundred and fifty bamboos used in its construction were buried in sand from the beach for six months to preserve them from attacks by the bamboo bugs. The work on the organ was finished in 1862, after forty-four years of labor, love, and patience; the average lifetime, perhaps, of a Filipino. Twice, the organ was badly damaged: in 1862 by an earthquake; and in 1882 by rains, when the church roof was blown off by a typhoon. It was partially repaired.

In 1917, Father Fanial, a Belgian missionary, completed the repairs of the instrument with the help of the Las Piñas people. An electric blower was installed in 1932, and the organ was completely repaired again in 1943.

We entered Las Piñas Church and dropped our offering in the box; this money is used to keep the instrument in repair. We walked up the stairs to the balcony. A small boy, perhaps twelve years old, came to play this famous old organ for us. He manipulated the stops projected on a panel in front of him, touching them lightly with his finger tips. We stood enthralled; for out of those ancient bamboo pipes, came soft sweet tones, unlike organ music any place on earth.

Chapter Twenty-Three

WHEN WE RETURNED from our trip, we found the household languishing, even to JoJo, the cat, who was a regular Filipino, and lived on fish and rice. I had not foreseen a rice famine in Manila, so it had not occurred to me to lay in a supply from the army commissary. Besides, Josie had always taken care of the rice purchases.

We had left the pantry well-stocked with canned fruits, vegetables, and meats, and there was a charge account at the Luzon Market where Josie could buy anything she needed. She had complete control of the kitchen. I had taught her to check the bills each day, and the Chinese man who owned the store respected her ability. She paid the grocery bill at the end of the month, and she paid the telephone bill at the American Embassy building. On several occasions we even sent her to the Bank of New York to make deposits. She had been the guardian of our household, able to handle any situation—but she could not cope with the rice shortage.

Josie and Julie liked American food, but Benita, the lavandera, simply could not eat bread; she must have rice. When we arrived home, Josie was squatting over the little Filipino washtub, doing the laundry while Benita languished on a mat. José was so weak he couldn't coconut the floors. There were ham and eggs in the refrigerator, but José needed rice. So he took off for his uncle's place up near Pampanga. Josie warned him the Huks would probably shoot off his hat while he was pounding palay, but he was willing to risk his head and his hat just for a bowl of rice.

Josie told me the Maynards, across the way, had a two-hundred-pound sack of rice they had bought at the army commissary. I hurried her over with a two-gallon bucket to borrow that amount; I would put in for our allotment and repay the loan.

Soon our household was humming again. The rice was boiling. JoJo was right under Josie's feet sniffing that good smell of rice, and Benita was standing patiently by, with three small smelly dried fish. After she had eaten her rice and fish, she was able to resume doing the daily laundry. This chore was essential because of the heat. The bed linens were changed every day, and Huddy's shirts and our dresses were changed several times a day.

When our two-hundred-pound sack of rice arrived, the girls neglected their household duties to care for it. They stretched a large tarpaulin on the grass and spread the rice to dry in the sun, otherwise it might mildew. They took turns standing over the supply, watching it carefully lest a covey of little rice birds swoop down and steal a few grains.

This drying ceremony, which lasted several days, drew a crowd of spectators: the Filipino Embassy guards and others in the compound. It was such a great heap of rice. Two hundred pounds! The average Filipino who works in the city is content to make enough centavos in one day to buy just one ganto of rice.

Then came the winnowing. It was a pretty sight to watch the girls lift large bamboo trays filled with rice high above their heads, then let it spill to earth like a golden waterfall. The wind from the bay cleared it of husks. After the winnowing, the rice was placed in coffee cans, buckets, anything with a tight-fitting lid to keep out the mice and weevils.

Once more we had a happy household, for we had rice. The next day, a dilapidated old jeepney loaded with squawking chickens and squealing pigs rattled up in front of our quonset.

Soon there was bedlam downstairs. José had come home, and brought his uncle, chickens, and pigs.

Two days after José had returned to his province, the Huks had raided his uncle's home. They had taken the rice supply, killed the carabao for meat, stolen clothes, and set fire to the nipa hut. The chickens and pigs had been out in the field, and the dissidents had not taken the time to catch them. José had assured his uncle that he would be welcome to live underneath the quonset hut in the Embassy Compound. And they would be safe because a guard walked the sea wall day and night.

I remembered our experience with Ilocos and Neighbor, so I asked José to take the chickens and pigs and the old jeepney to his cousins who lived in Pasay. He had such a sorrowful look in his eyes, then asked: "Mom, what about uncle? Could he sleep here? He makes no noise like a rooster?"

I was considered a rebel by my fellow Americans, for I was always losing face, in their opinion. And, likely, if the Ambassador should discover this small barrio underneath my quonset hut, I might get orders to vacate the dignified compound. But how could I turn the old man away? He had been ravaged by the Huks. So I told José to fix a place for him to sleep.

That evening when I went down to water the flowers, he had watered them and was down on his knees weeding the plants with loving hands. Just let Neighbor say one word to me and I would say: "The man is our new gardener."

A few days later he moved to Pasay with the cousins. He had found work.

In the years that Josie was with us, I spoke crossly to her only once. I recall it with shame. It was a particularly hot day and I had been out gathering news for my column. Usually I ate lunch at the Manila Overseas Press Club, but on this day I decided to go home. I found the house very untidy; not a bed was made, nor a dish washed. And where was Josie? I went down to the laundry room to question Benita. When she saw I was angry, she started to cry; she was sure something dreadful had happened to Josie. She had dressed and left early with a cousin. She was to be back by eleven o'clock. And Josie always made good a promise, so Benita reminded me.

I was in a bad mood, so I started to wash the dishes myself, but first I had to pour boiling water over the ants that were crawling over them. My compatriots were right! I *had* lost face because I had indulged my girls. I had four people working for me, and here I was killing ants! When Benita heard me slamming things in the kitchen, she left her ironing and came up to take over.

Just at this moment, Josie came rolling up in a taxi. I didn't let her come upstairs but yelled out: "You're fired, Josie!" I remember the tears came into her eyes as she tried to explain. "But Mom!" she pleaded. "Don't you Mom me!" I told her to go and never come back. She reentered the taxi and drove away. Benita sensed my injustice and started to cry again. "Poor Josie. She's a good girl, Mom."

Then I started to cry. I rushed to the telephone to ask the guard to halt the taxi at the gate. I was too late. The car had already passed through and was speeding up the boulevard.

I was so ashamed of my behavior. I tumbled face down upon the bed. I heard Julie when she came home; I could hear Benita talking to her in Tagalog, no doubt telling her what an old ogre I had turned out to be. Julie, quite unruffled, set about to clean the house. Then I could hear her pounding garlic buds; she was going to cook pork adobo for dinner, my favorite dish.

I was lying very quietly in my bed, trying to console myself that I had a right to blow my top occasionally. Soon Julie came to my bedside: "Mom, for you I bring the calamansi juice." Josie always brought this cool drink of lime juice to me when I was tired. Dear, sweet Josie. I thanked Julie, without looking her in the eyes, and took the glass. Pretty soon Benita came padding into the bedroom, ever so quietly, as if someone had just died. She placed my freshly ironed dresses in the closet.

Julie came again to inquire if I needed anything. Yes, I needed Josie, but I wouldn't say so, nor would I ask any questions. She went back in the kitchen and I could smell the delicious adobo.

Around five-thirty I heard Huddy's car drive in. How could I face him? He was very fond of Josie. Perhaps I could send him to fetch her, so I could apologize. I heard a voice say: "Sir, sit down here in the sun porch and I'll go up and get a cold beer for you." It was Josie's voice . . . Josie's footsteps were coming up the stairway! Josie was back!

After my display of temper she had gone directly to the doctor's office to tell him what had happened. She was sure that I was sick, or very tired. Did he want her to leave? If so, she would go. My dear husband had put her in the car and had brought her home and given her a ten peso raise. I tried to apologize but she would not let me. "It was my fault, Mom." She had gone to attend a morning mass at Malate Church in memory of her mother. She had forgotten to tell me before I left home, and the services had lasted much longer than she had expected.

Our tour of duty for the government would soon be over. Huddy's health was failing, so we knew we must return to the States. But we worried about our little Filipino family. José had been attending the Mission School for several months but he wanted to return to his province and be a rice farmer. His problem was solved. What about our girls? They were smart and pretty. All they needed was a chance. Their young hearts cried out for the finer things in life; and we wanted to help them.

When we took long drives on Sunday to Tagaytay, to Lipa, or to Pagsanjan Falls, they went along. There was no reason why they could not enjoy the drives and the countryside. Yet, often I was criticized for this. When the *President Cleveland* made its first trip to Manila after the war, I went to a cocktail party on board. When I told Josie about the luxury of the ship, she wished she might someday be able to see it.

The time came. Several months later, the *Cleveland* docked again, and on this occasion my friend, Wilma Wolfe, was sailing for the States. She wanted to take her housegirl, Mary, to see the luxurious ship and to bid her goodbye. Wilma asked if I would come down to the *President Cleveland* to see her off and return Mary to her home in Pasay. I went to the steamship line office to get three passes—for Josie, Julie, and Benita. The girls were so happy. At last they were to go aboard the big passenger liner. Josie and Julie looked so pretty in their new dresses and shoes. Benita was very dignified looking in a blue terno. She had no shoes, except bakyas, so she borrowed a pair from Josie.

As they walked up the gangplank, they resembled a mother and her two daughters. On this night they had the run of the *Cleveland,* the same as the mayor and his wife, or the President of the Philippines. For days they talked about the wonderful time they had on board the ship. Our girls told the story over and over to their friends who worked in the Embassy Compound quonset huts. I am sure dear Benita told the story to her grand-children when she went home that night.

It had been Josie's dream to attend a School of Design and learn to be a dressmaker. The Filipina women are expert seam-stresses; many of them make a comfortable living at this pro-fession. Josie was a natural with the needle. But she was resigned to the fact that her dream would never be a reality; she had to help support a younger brother and a sick father.

Huddy and I worked out a schedule. Josie could leave at the lunch hour to go to dressmaking school. Julie didn't return from the Mission School until after one o'clock. The housework would have to be organized so it could be done in the forenoon, and I would help with it whenever necessary.

When I told Josie that she could start school she looked straight at me, then exclaimed: "Oh, Mom!" I shall never forget the look of gratitude that enveloped her face. Dear Josie. I knew in that moment I was repaid for every small act of kindness that I had ever done. Quickly the joyous look faded. She argued that she had "many works to do" and that she would not permit me to lose face.

Nevertheless, we hustled Josie off to school. She looked so pretty in her white linen dress and white shoes, with her dark hair piled high on her head. She carried her notebooks and pencils and a hundred peso bill in her pocket book for her tuition fee. She walked up the road in the Embassy Compound with her head held high. My heart was filled with pride as if my own little girl were starting her first day at school. At the corner she turned and waved to me. I shall hold that picture in my mind forever.

When I went back inside the quonset, my friend from across the street came running in. She informed me I was setting a very bad example in the Embassy Compound. Her housegirl knew that Josie was going to school. Now she had set up a howl to start to a school. My friend said she would never permit it; she hired her girls to be servants and to wait on her.

"You are doing these girls a great injustice. What will they do when you return to the States? Let them remain servants; that's what they were meant to be."

When Julie returned from the Mission School, she came immediately to my studio. She sidled up to me holding something behind her. "Mom," she said, then tears filled her eyes and her voice choked.

"Yes, Julie?" I said.

"Mom," then she burst into tears. "Oh, Mom, Josie—Josie —she always wanted so much to go to dressmaking school." Then she rushed toward me and placed around my neck a lei of sweet sampaguita. It was her way of saying, "Thank you, Mom, for Josie."

Chapter Twenty-Four

☙ THE *President Cleveland* weighed anchor again. Huddy, Harvel, and I were sailing for home. Josie, Julie, and Benita were standing on the pier waving goodbye through their tears.

Later, I stood alone on deck as the ship moved out to sea, and watched the skyline of Manila fade away. I wept, for I was leaving part of my heart in the Philippines.

I went to our stateroom where Huddy was resting in bed. He had suffered a severe coronary thrombosis and was being returned to the States for hospitalization. I told him about my last glimpse of Manila . . . the Army and Navy Club and our little quonset by the sea. He smiled; we both knew these years in the Philippines had been the happiest ones of our lives, though the most strenuous for him. My heart was desolate because I knew the final answer—the doctors at Ft. William McKinley Hospital had prepared me.

There was a port call at glamorous old Hong Kong. Then we sailed on past Formosa and docked at Kobe, Japan. Here, a two-day tour was planned for the passengers. They could board a bus at Kobe and have an overland trip in Japan and return to the ship when it docked at Yokohama. I had seen Japan in the glory of cherry blossom time; I had stood in awe at the foot of snow-capped Fujiyama; I had danced in glee with the geisha girls at a suki-yaki at old Kyoto. Now I should like to say goodbye to Japan.

Huddy assured me the ship's hospital staff and Harvel would

look after him and that I should join the group of fourteen Americans to make this tour. This trip was a memorable one and brought me one of the strangest and most touching experiences of my life. We were on the last lap of the tour, going from Tokyo to Kamakura to view "Old Daibutsu," the Great Buddha. We were racing with time for we wanted to arrive before sundown so we might get shots on color film.

As one approaches this imposing shrine, there are many shops selling trinkets to tourists, so we paused briefly at a place selling "Views of Kamakura." The sun was setting, so I suggested we go on to make our film. As we started, the little gray-haired proprietress of the shop stepped in front of the group.

There were several women younger and prettier than I, others older and wiser, yet she walked straight up to me and gently laid her hand on my shoulder. "You go soon to America?" she asked. Perhaps it was the sad tone in her voice, or was it the tears in her eyes? Whatever it was, I remained while my friends rushed on toward the Great Buddha. I could hear their cameras clicking and their voices urging me to hurry on. I could see the sun sinking lower and lower. Yet I lingered with this little gray-haired woman whom I had never seen, nor, probably, would ever see again.

With complete abandon she told her story: somewhere in America was her husband's grave. He had died in a Japanese detention camp. If I should come across his grave, would I say a little prayer for him?

I glanced at the Great Buddha with the fire shrines burning and at the Japanese kneeling in prayer. Down the way was the famous Hachiman Shrine; men dressed in rich brocades and carrying strange objects of worship were hurrying toward it. How did one pray for a dead Japanese? It seemed she read my thoughts for quickly she said: "Just a little prayer your way. A little American prayer."

I promised that should I ever come upon his grave, I would

carry out her wishes. She gave me a little envelope with "Views of Kamakura," and on the back she wrote in a fine handwriting: D. Yoshikawa. I was to search for this name.

The sun was down. My friends were disgusted because I had not hurried on to make color films. And what on earth did the Japanese woman want with me? I could not tell them what she had asked me to do. They might laugh at her or at the thought of my searching for a lonely grave of a Japanese detentionee somewhere in America.

I have never forgotten the little woman back in Kamakura. I can still see every wrinkle in her face and can even remember the floral pattern of the Japanese kimono she wore that day. It was many months later, back in Santa Fé, New Mexico, that Huddy and I came upon the barren graves by the side of the road, not far from the old Japanese Detention Camp. I was driving the car and it was Huddy who sighted the Japanese symbols chiseled in the stone. He asked me to stop the car and check the headstones. I had told him about the little woman in Kamakura.

I shall always remember the bigness of his heart. He was lamed by his years of service in the Philippines, trying, in his small way, to help heal the wounds of its people . . . wounds inflicted by the Japanese. Perhaps his tolerance came from his training: medicine knows no race, no creed. Perhaps it was his theory: we had fought for a principle and won; now we should be big enough to reach out a hand to the Japanese and help them grasp the truth of our teachings.

I crawled through the barbed wire fence and waded deep snow to reach the desolate graves. Under the Japanese symbols were carved the names of the deceased. One tomb bore the inscription: D. Yoshikawa, died June 5, 1945. There may be as many Yoshikawas in Japan as we have Smiths and Browns in America, but I like to believe that this was the grave so dear to the heart of the little woman back in old Kamakura.

I placed my hand on the cold slab that marked the lonely grave of this Japanese, and softly repeated the Lord's Prayer . . . "forgive us our trespasses as we forgive those who trespass against us."

The ocean voyage was uneventful. Harvel made friends with whom she played bridge in the afternoon, and danced in the evening. I remained very close to Huddy's side. We spent many hours in the sunshine on the top deck where JoJo, our cat, was kenneled. Huddy sat in the sunshine with him on his lap, a handsome animal in his red harness and leash given him by Doy Laurel as a "Bon Voyage" present. JoJo had grown into a very large cat. He measured forty inches from his ears to the tip of his tail. He couldn't possibly fit into one of the small kennels reserved for cats, so I rented a large one, bulldog-sized, so he would be comfortable.

JoJo was a fastidious eater. The day before we sailed, Josie and I had taken twenty-nine small tins of red salmon to my stateroom, for if the kennels served canned cat food, he would not eat it. I also took along a roll of waxed paper, and the first night out, I carried a piece to the dining room in which to wrap some of my lobster dinner for him. These tidbits, together with the salmon, would see him through the twenty-nine-day voyage.

When I entered the kennels with the lobster, that first night, Rickey, the kennel boy, asked: "What does JoJo like to eat?" I gazed upon a table loaded with lobster, chicken, and other good food from the dining room. These leftovers were fed to the animals, instead of being tossed overboard. Even then, JoJo was a problem cat; he liked rice with his fish. So I had to slip down to the third class section and bargain with the Chinese cook for bowls of rice.

One day when we were out in mid-Pacific, a little bird fell on deck right in front of the kennel door. It was too tired and too frightened to flutter a wing. We did not know where it had come from, for we were miles from land. Had it flown from a ship we had passed at sea? We never knew. Rickey rescued the little feathered one and found it had a broken wing, injured no doubt, when it flew against a wire mooring on deck.

I rushed down to get Huddy. He came to the top deck and very carefully put a splint on the little creature's wing. We made a bed out of a cigar box and placed the bird in the kennels. The barking of the dogs and the yowls of the cats frightened it, so Rickey took it to his bunk. The little bird died the next day. Rickey and Harvel wrapped it in a paper napkin; then I took a red silk scarf from my neck to use for a shroud. Gently tilting a board, we slid it over the rail and gave it a "burial at sea."

When we arrived in San Francisco, I gave Rickey the canned salmon, except for three cans which I took ashore for JoJo's dinner along with a bowl of rice from the Chinese cook. I felt very swanky as I walked into the St. Francis Hotel dressed in my best British tweeds bought in Hong Kong, and on my shoulder a beautiful black cat wearing a red harness. A few of the hotel guests rushed up to admire JoJo.

Suddenly the cat let out a yowl like a wild panther. He clawed my face and my hair and yanked the beret off my head. The paper bag I was carrying burst wide open, the rice spilled down the front of my suit, and the cans of salmon went rolling across the floor. A few of the people in the lobby thought the cat was a real black panther and took cover; others assumed I was just back from an African safari with a strange new pet; and others still gazing at the salmon rolling on the floor, no doubt thought I had just robbed a super market.

We had been informed in Honolulu that the St. Francis Hotel maintained kennels in the basement to care for pets. We had wired the hotel for such accommodations, but none were available. Two kind ladies, representing the Animal Shelter, with a booth in the lobby, rushed up to assist me with the frightened cat. They offered to take him to the A.S.P.C.A. Kennels on

Sixteenth Street for me. No sir! I would go with my cat! I had brought him safely thousands of miles and I'd stick with him. Besides, I wanted to inspect the kennels before I left my pet to be boarded.

Huddy was embarrassed over the cat's behaviour and my own. Nevertheless, I thrust my beret in his right hand and the remains of a bowl of rice in his left, with Harvel stacking the cans of salmon in the crook of an arm, while I rushed off in a taxi with howling JoJo to take him to the A.S.P.C.A.

Chapter Twenty-Five

๛ THERE IS a chain of memories that will forever bind me to the islands. I have a Christmas letter from Josie. "Dear Mom," she says, "I write to tell you that you left your footprints in the Philippines." I look at my hands. Do they have a dishpan look? My friend in the Embassy Compound told me so, whenever she caught me washing dishes so that Josie might attend school. No matter; my heart is filled with pride. For there is a little dress-making shop in the exclusive Ermita District in far-away Manila and the efficient proprietress is my faithful Josie, assisted by Julie. She is designing beautiful dresses for the very women who decreed she should sleep on a dirty mat and stand up to eat her rice for the rest of her days. I find myself hoping these women are forced to pay high prices for Josie's expert workmanship. But knowing this girl, who was a part of our household for over four years, I am sure she is turning out excellent designs at "live and let live" prices.

Josie's letter brought back happy memories. Strange, as I read it I should think of "Adam." Perhaps it was because "Adam," like Josie, played a great part in my knowing so intimately the Philippines and its people. I am sure that long ago the old army jeep, like so many other wrecks, was rolled over the cliffs to a watery grave.

I move about my studio and touch the rattan furniture that

I brought home from the Philippines. I pause by the little native stove over which we boiled rice; now the pot contains a fern. There is a big brass meat tray from the Moro country, once used by a Datu, and beautiful wood carvings by the Igorots, a miniature calesa—I used to ride a bright red one down Ong Ping Street to visit Chinatown. These mementos bring me very close to my beloved Philippines. I smile as I pick up a spear from the headhunter country. I am recalling the time a huge rat invaded the quonset. The rodent was bigger than JoJo; in fact, it was when it attacked the cat that Josie and I grabbed the spears and went into action. By the time we had annihilated the rat, the quonset looked as if the Huks had raided it. There were broken dishes, broken Chinese vases, chairs upset, and JoJo with a badly bitten front paw. We had had to rush him to the Army Veterinarian for treatment.

I pause beside my big desk. It once was used by General Jonathan Wainwright. How did it come into my possession? It was Huddy's desk, an old army number assigned to the Veterans Administration, a large spacious one such as he liked. But the U.S. Government decided to discard the old office furniture and install new desks made of Philippine mahogany. So Huddy's desk was placed, along with others, on the "pile," to be disposed of. Often these discards are burned, so I asked General Lovett if I might have a desk to use in my studio. He said that I could have any one I chose, but I would have to pay the transportation from the Heacock Building to our quonset. I picked out Huddy's old desk from the pile and had it sent to the Embassy Compound. Later, when we were cleaning it up to give it a coat of varnish, we found the identification sticker which was pasted in one of the drawers. Huddy was as surprised as I when we discovered he had been sitting for months at General Wainwright's desk. We kept very quiet about this discovery. I used the desk in my studio during the remainder of our stay, and it was shipped back to the States with our furniture at government expense.

When we arrived back in San Antonio, Texas, our home base, General Wainwright was living there and had an insurance agency. I called him and told him I had brought home his desk, and related the circumstances. I offered to return it to him.

"No, my dear," he said. "I want you to keep it."

The old desk is war-weary, battered, and just about to fall apart. But I seem to write best when seated at it. When Huddy offered to get me a new, modern desk, I would not hear of it, for then I probably could not write at all.

Huddy was hospitalized at Brook General, Ft. Sam Houston, suffering from another severe coronary thrombosis when the news reached us that Ramón Magsaysay was in the race for the presidency of the Philippines. I hurried out to the hospital with a copy of our daily *Manila Bulletin* and read the good news to him.

"That's my boy! and I am betting on him!" he said. Huddy believed from the very beginning of the campaign that Ramón would win, even though he was aware that politics in the Philippines are often upredictable. Step by step we followed the bitter political fight between President Quirino and Ramón. Often we would laugh together as we visualized "our boy" riding in a calesa through the small barrios waving a cheerful "Hello!" to his people with his generous sincere grin reaching from ear to ear; we could see him stalking through a rice paddy to greet an old friend, a wrinkle-faced farmer. Yes, our hearts and our prayers followed him. Here was a man with a deep-hearted sympathy for the common people; he was one of them; he had first-hand information and knowledge of their problems. Here was a man who might bring prosperity back to the islands; a man who could fill the rice bowls; a man who believed the little man was entitled to more food in his stomach, more clothing on his back, a better roof over his head.

It was months later. Our family was separated. Harvel was now a hostess on Braniff Airlines flying out of Dallas. Huddy had been discharged from the hospital and we had returned to our original home in Santa Fé, New Mexico. The Philippine election was drawing closer. Day after day, Huddy sat near a short-wave radio following the events in far-away Manila. The night before the election, he said to me, "I'm going to go to bed early, for tomorrow I'm going to stay up all night long just to hear that 'my boy' has been elected President of the Philippines!"

Our hearts were filled with pride for Ramón. We knew he was a happy man with his adored family, and now he might be able to confer upon his beautiful wife, Luz, the highest honor to come to any woman in the Philippines—First Lady of the Land. His daughters and son, Teresita, Milagros, and Ramón, Jr., might say with pride: "Our father is President of the Philippines!"

At four o'clock the next morning Huddy was gone. He went very quickly, of a heart attack.

Night came. In the Philippines, it was Election Day. I went alone to the study and turned on the radio. I was too grief-stricken to care about details . . . I heard voices . . . music . . . confusion. Then, just at daybreak, the big news came. I called out: "Oh, darling! Your boy has made it!" Then I turned to face the empty chair. Huddy had gone away just twenty-four hours before Ramón Magsaysay was elected President of the Philippines.

The Doctor had been greatly concerned about the Philippines. He contended a great nation must be a happy nation, but could there be happiness when there was so much poverty and hunger and inequality? In our travels through the islands, we had known the very very rich and the very very poor. There seemed to be no in-between. He realized the intense need for land and social reform.

In his work with the Filipino veterans he had gained a keen insight into what the Filipinos wanted, what they needed . . . dignity and identity as a nation. He respected their dignity as a people. He even refused to refer to our household help as servants.

There was a sign at the entrance to the Army and Navy Club which read: "No Filipinos Allowed." We resented it. Once we had a Filipina visitor from Iloilo City. We wanted to take her to dinner at the club and she was looking forward to it, too. The Doctor was a member and most certainly entitled to take any guest he invited. What about the sign? When we arrived at the club, I hurried up the steps ahead of them and rather nonchalantly backed up against it to conceal it from her while he escorted her by.

He also believed the Philippines must find itself as a nation. It was his hope there should come a re-evaluation of the true Filipino culture, a return to a true national dignity, a new maturity that would bring with it an acceptance of the Filipino as a Filipino, and not as the "Little Brown Brother" of America.

With Ramón Magsaysay as president, I felt sure the Philippines would come into its own.

Ramón never forgot a friend. After the Doctor's death, I received from him greetings each Christmas and each Decoration Day. Only once did I ask a favor of him as President. My friend Major Gene Baca, who had served as liaison officer at Malacañang Palace during the war, had friends from Texas, the Judson Colliers, who were flying to Manila. The major wanted them to be able to visit the palace where he had once served. He came to me about it. "You are a good friend of the President. Would you ask him to see that the Colliers are shown through the palace?"

I wrote a letter to Ramón asking this favor of him. He immediately sent me the following telegram. Its formality amused me: "HAVE ORDERED ONE OF MY AIDES TO MEET

MR AND MRS JUDSON COLLIER UPON THEIR AR-
RIVAL MANILA JUNE EIGHT STOP HAVE ASKED MR
BACA FOR MORE DETAILS STOP CORDIAL RE-
GARDS—
PRESIDENT MAGSAYSAY"

Major Baca and I worked out the details the President had
requested and sent him a telegram. When the Collier's plane
arrived at the International Airport, Ramon Magsaysay was on
hand to meet them. They were overwhelmed, for he had brought
along the official band from Malacañang Palace and when they
stepped from the plane, the band struck up: "The Yellow Rose
of Texas." They rode with him in the Presidential limousine to
the Manila Hotel.

That's what the President of the Philippines was like—that
boy from Zambales who had crawled underneath "Old Diablo"
to get the wicks adjusted so I would not have to throw a
tantrum!

The last message I received from Ramón Magsaysay was a
note with a small package which contained a little bouquet of
yellow flowers, the Everlasting Flowers of Baguio, tied with the
colors of the Philippine Republic. This was on a Saturday March
16, 1957. I drove out to the National Cemetery in old Santa
Fe to place the offering on the Doctor's grave, I took a flower
from the bouquet as a little memento to take back to my studio.
When I returned to the car, I placed it with the note on the car
seat and started home. I turned on the radio to get the news.
Suddenly, like a blast, came a bulletin: RAMON MAG-
SAYSAY, PRESIDENT OF THE PHILIPPINES, KILLED
IN A PLANE CRASH OVER THE ISLAND OF CEBU.

Truth is indeed stranger than fiction! My impulse was to
rush back to Huddy's grave and cry out: "Your boy . . . your
boy is dead!" instead, I drove straight to the cathedral in down-
town Sante Fe. I picked up the flower and re-read the note from
Ramón: "Today I went to the Archbishop's Place in Mandalu-

yong and said a prayer for the dear Doctor." Sorrowfully and tearfully, I entered the cathedral. At the altar I lighted a candle and placed beside it the little yellow flower from the Philippines. I knelt, and in my humble way, said a prayer for my dear friend, Ramón.

Today the Republic of the Philippines lives in the shadow of Communist China. It must meet this threat head-on. How? In 1955, on July 4, which is the Philippine Independence Day, as also that of the United States, Ramón Magsaysay made a public address. I shall quote it.

"Let me say here and now that we cannot flirt with communism, if we want our independence to remain real and secure . . . Only on this basis can we shape and build the kind of Philippines that you, here in this room, and the millions who have agreed with the principles I set forth during the presidential campaign, want for yourselves and your children. Our people want a Philippines strong and stable internally and able to preserve its hard-won independence against external threats, in firm alliance with our great and good friend the United States of America."

May God bless the Philippines!